RA 971.8.W4

CARING
IN A
CRISIS

KU-068-938

Going home
from hospital

Sheila White

WITHDRAWN

Health Library
Clinical Education Centre
ST4 6QG

College of Nursing & Midwifery
City General Hospital
Newcastle Road
Stoke-on-Trent ST4 6QG

ACE
BOOKS

For my parents

©1994 Sheila White
Published by Age Concern England
1268 London Road
London SW16 4ER

Editor Caroline Hartnell
Production Marion Peat
Design and typesetting Eugenie Dodd Typographics
Printed in Great Britain by Bell & Bain Ltd, Glasgow

A catalogue record for this book is available from the British Library.

ISBN 0–86242–155–1

All rights reserved; no part of this work may be reproduced
in any form, by mimeograph or any other means, without
permission in writing from the publisher.

Contents

About the author

Sheila White is a freelance writer and editor. She has written material for carers of people with advanced cancer for the cancer charity BACUP and has contributed to a number of publications for carers including *Caring at Home*.

Acknowledgements

Many people have generously given me their advice and time to help me write this book. In particular, I would like to thank:

Geraldine Amos and Yvonne Smith, Home from Hospital.

Olive Elborough and the Alzheimers Carers Support Group, Kingston-upon-Thames.

Chris Gray, Kingston Carers Network.

Jill Harrison, Carers National Association.

Chris Maison, SEN, Brentford and Chiswick Community Health Services.

Dr Finbarr Martin, Consultant Geriatrician, St Thomas's Hospital.

Carol Miruszenko, Social Work Department, Solihull Hospital.

I would also like to thank Barbara Meredith of Age Concern for giving me the benefit of her expertise and Caroline Hartnell for her careful editing.

Finally, my personal thanks go to Kevin McGeoghegan for keeping me going, and to our families and friends for all their help and support.

Introduction

This book is for anyone who is going to be caring for someone when they come out of hospital. The person you are caring for is most likely to be your parent or partner. But you may find yourself looking after a grandparent, sister or brother, aunt or uncle, friend or neighbour. The kind of care they might need will depend on why they went into hospital, their underlying state of health, and whether or not they live alone.

There are just as many different kinds of carer as there are people being cared for. You might not even have thought of yourself as a carer until the person you are going to look after went into hospital. Or you might already be caring for them at home. You might be going to care for them permanently or just for the first few weeks after they come out of hospital. You might live hundreds of miles away or just round the corner.

The situation you find yourself in might depend on whether their admission to hospital was planned or unplanned. For example, if someone is booked to go into hospital for an operation, there should be time before admission to think ahead to any arrangements that might need to be made for when they come out. But if someone is admitted in an emergency, after a fall or stroke for example, any planning will have to take place as soon as possible after the initial crisis is over.

This book is written for you, whatever your situation. It aims to help you prepare for when the person you care for comes out of hospital and to make sure that you both get involved in deciding what happens to them afterwards.

Chapter 1 explains what hospital discharge is and summarises the Government guidelines on what should be done before someone leaves hospital.

Chapter 2 is about preparing for when someone leaves hospital and how you, as a carer, can get involved in this process. It looks at ways in which the hospital staff and other professionals should help patients plan for going home and the kinds of things that can be arranged in advance. It also considers the temporary options that might be open to them if they can't go straight home: staying with you or another friend or relative for a while, or convalescence.

Chapter 3 describes the kind of help that someone coming out of hospital might need and explains who can provide it.

Chapter 4 takes a step-by-step look at what should happen on the day they go home.

Chapter 5 looks at the help with money that might be available both for the person you are looking after and for you as carer. It also tells you what to do if you need to manage someone else's financial affairs for them.

In this book the person you are caring for will be referred to as 'your relative', but they could equally be a friend or neighbour. The person you care for will also be referred to as 'she', but everything in the book applies equally to both sexes.

Hospital discharge – what is it?

By the time you are reading this book, your relative may be starting to recover. You may be feeling exhausted from the strain of having someone you care for in hospital, especially if she has been critically ill or has had a major operation.

If your relative's admission to hospital was planned, arrangements for her discharge should already have been discussed. If she was admitted unexpectedly, this is the time when everyone involved – your relative, yourself, the hospital staff, your relative's GP, friends, family and neighbours – should start to consider whether she will need any help when she goes home.

This chapter explains what hospital discharge involves and outlines the standards that hospitals should meet when patients leave their care. It explains the difference between planned and unplanned admissions, and what to do if you or your relative thinks she is being discharged too early.

DOROTHY

6 We had a very good hospital social worker, Glynis, who spent a lot of time talking to me about what help I thought we needed. 9

'I've lived with my mother-in-law, Anne, for 37 years. She's 95 now and very frail and unsteady. During the last ten years she's had a heart attack, a total hip replacement and cataract operations. She also has osteoporosis, arthritis in her left knee and poor eyesight and hearing. She's doubly incontinent and needs help with bathing and dressing. In June last year she had one of her falls, but this time she broke her leg and had to go to hospital. Her leg was in plaster for 12 weeks but didn't seem to be healing, and the doctor told me that it was unlikely she would walk again. She needed lifting with a hoist and regular turning to make sure she didn't get bed sores.

'I was keen to continue to nurse her at home – I'd always promised to care for her and I love her dearly. My own mother died when I was ten so she's been a substitute mother for me. But I'm a widow now and I have to work full-time. We couldn't manage without my income. My stepdaughter helps me out but we were obviously going to need a lot more help from outside.

'Fortunately, we had a very good hospital social worker, Glynis, who spent a lot of time talking to me about what help I thought we needed. She arranged a meeting at the hospital for me, the occupational therapist, the district nurse liaison officer, the community social worker and the ward sister. Anne was so frail and confused at that stage that she didn't come to the meeting, but Glynis and I talked with her afterwards and she seemed to understand what we were saying. She made it clear she didn't want to go into a home, anyway.

'I already had a lot of equipment at home – a zimmer frame, a wheelchair, incontinence pads, a board under her mattress, two commodes (one for upstairs and one for downstairs) and a bedpan. But the occupational therapist and district nurse liaison officer came to see what else we would need. We decided we would also need a Nimbus mattress, a hoist and sling, a feeding cup, a back rest and a table to go over her bed.

'Glynis worked out a rota of care for Anne. She arranged for me to have help from the district nurses, a private nursing agency and Crossroads.

All the equipment I needed was ready for when Anne came home. The occupational therapist showed me how to use the hoist, and I spent some invaluable time on the ward watching how the nurses cared for her.

'Before Anne was discharged, Glynis organised a final meeting of everyone involved. Anne came home at the beginning of October. It was very hard work at first, but six months later Anne is much stronger and better in herself. We've cut down the hours of the private nurse and the district nurses don't need to come so frequently.

'It's lovely to see Anne so happy. She likes a glass of wine with me in the evening and she enjoys having company.'

What is hospital discharge?

When your relative leaves hospital she will be discharged. This means that the doctor in charge of her care – usually the consultant – is satisfied that she is well enough to leave the hospital. No patient can be discharged without the authority of the doctor responsible for her care.

Patients leaving hospital often feel that they are almost incidental to the whole discharge process, and as a carer you may feel even more peripheral. The Government has, however, drawn up guidelines on hospital discharge that make it clear that before anyone leaves hospital there should be a full discussion about what help they will need and who is going to provide it. Your relative should be at the centre of this discussion. As her main carer, you have the right to be involved too.

The following box summarises Government guidelines for local authorities and health authorities. These were set out in full in two Department of Health circulars (LAC(89)7 and HC(89)5), and an accompanying booklet *Discharge of Patients from Hospital*. The *Hospital Discharge Workbook*, published in 1994, sets out a framework for good practice based on Government policy on hospital discharge arrangements set out in these earlier circulars (details on p 16). We will be referring to these guidelines throughout the book.

1. The hospital should make sure that it has an agreed discharge procedure and that all the hospital staff have been informed of it.

2. A specific member of staff should have responsibility for checking that all the procedures have been followed before a patient is discharged.

3. If someone leaving hospital needs help afterwards, planning for this should begin as early as possible.

4. Patients' home situations should be assessed, and any support, help or equipment they need should be arranged before they are discharged.

5. Any adaptations to a patient's home should have been made – or at least a firm timetable agreed with the local authority – before they are discharged.

6. Patients – and, if the patient gives consent, relatives or carers – should be consulted and informed at every stage and before decisions are made.

7. The hospital should make sure that patients understand the arrangements being proposed, including patients with partial sight or hearing or for whom English is a second language.

8. Arrangements should be made for information about patients to go to their GP, district nurse, care manager, etc, in good time.

9. The hospital should take any special action needed when a patient is discharged at or immediately before a weekend or bank holiday, or late in the day.

The guidelines also state that *special care* should be taken when discharging patients:

▶ who live alone, and/or who are frail and/or elderly, or live with an elderly carer;

▶ who have a serious illness or a continuing disability;

▶ who are terminally ill;

▶ who suffer from a psychiatric illness;

▶ who have been in hospital for an extended stay;

▶ who are in need of special help, eg who are incontinent or will need nursing or other kinds of care at home;

▶ who have communication difficulties.

The Government has produced a *Patient's Charter*, which outlines patients' rights and the standards that the health services should meet. The section on hospital discharge says:

'. . . before you are discharged from hospital a decision should be made about any continuing health or social care needs you may have. Your hospital will agree arrangements for meeting these needs with agencies such as community nursing services and local authority social services departments before you are discharged. You and, with your agreement, your carers will be consulted and informed at all stages.'

Some hospitals have made great efforts to improve the way that people are discharged. They have home treatment teams or hospital aftercare schemes to ensure that patients who are going home continue to receive all the care they need to manage, at least for the first few weeks.

The Government also believes that local authorities should produce their own Community Care Charters by the end of 1995 and has produced draft guidance for local authorities to use as a framework. These Charters may include information about hospital discharge arrangements so that assessments for services people might need when discharged are carried out in good time and to high standards. This should help ensure that, for example, arrangements for care are in place before discharge so services can start as soon as a patient leaves hospital.

Planned and unplanned admission

Your relative's experience of hospital discharge may depend to some extent on whether or not her admission to hospital was planned.

Planned admission

If your relative knew well in advance that she was going into hospital, for example for a coronary bypass operation, you may have had an opportunity to discuss together any arrangements that need to be made before she went in. Ideally, the hospital staff will also have started planning her discharge before admission. Government guidelines on good practice say: *'For non-emergency cases where it is known that support will be required on discharge, planning should start before admission.'*

Unplanned admission

Hospital staff should start planning for discharge as soon as possible when someone is admitted unexpectedly or in an emergency.

Sometimes people are discharged directly from an accident and emergency (A&E) department without going on to another ward. In this case, the Government has said that there should still be an agreed procedure for planning patients' discharge and that a nominated member of staff should be responsible for ensuring that the procedure is carried out. Discharge procedure should include:

▶ letting patients' GPs know they have been admitted;

▶ making sure transport home is provided if needed;

▶ ensuring that no one goes back to an empty home without support if they need it;

▶ telling patients what to do if their condition deteriorates after they have been discharged.

Early discharge

Nowadays, hospital stays are generally shorter than they used to be. This is partly because with modern medicine people tend to recover more quickly. But it is also because hospitals are often under pressure to treat as many patients as they can. For some people, this can mean that they have to leave hospital before they have recovered fully.

ANNIE

❛I don't know why they were in such a hurry to send him home before he was ready.❜

'My next-door neighbour went into hospital two weeks before Christmas for tests because he was complaining of chest pains. He's 83 but lives on his own and looks after himself. I keep an eye on him but I'm 75 and have arthritis so I can't do much. People from church visit sometimes and he goes to the Sunday service. He's got a son in Canada and a nephew in Wales.

'Anyway, I visited him several times in hospital and the day before Christmas Eve he told me the doctor had said he could go home the next day. He was very worried about this as he still had the chest pains, although the tests hadn't come up with anything. He'd said this to the doctor but he'd been told that there was no need for him to be in hospital and that his GP would visit him at home.

'He came home in an ambulance on Christmas Eve and I made sure he had enough food and was all right. I rang the church for him and told them what had happened and they said someone would call in on him. I went to my daughter's for Christmas and wasn't back till the day after Boxing Day.

'Someone from the church did call on him but not until Boxing Day. The police had to break the door down in the end – he'd tried to take an overdose. The GP didn't even know he was home.

'He went straight back into hospital and stayed in for another two weeks. During that time, they sorted out all kinds of things. They decided that there was nothing wrong with his heart but that the chest pains were probably caused by anxiety. Social services organised for him to have meals on wheels and a home help. He also goes to an Age Concern centre once a week where he can have a hot meal and a bit of company. Someone from the church comes once a week and I call in as often as I can. His nephew rings once a week from Wales and visits once a month.

'I don't know why they were in such a hurry to send him home before he was ready.'

Like Annie's neighbour, many people, particularly older people, feel alarmed when they are told they can go home, especially if they live alone or with another older or disabled person. After a serious illness, fall or operation, they may not have the strength or confidence to leave the security of the ward so soon.

Sometimes the hospital staff are keen to get patients home again before they lose all their independence, even if that means risking an unplanned readmission. Providing patients are given all the help and support they need, this might be the best course of action. But if your relative seems genuinely anxious about leaving hospital so soon, one or both of you needs to say so (see pp 36–37 for more on standing up for yourself).

What to do if you think discharge is too early

1 Talk to the ward sister. Try to make it clear that while you respect the medical judgement of the doctors and nurses, your relative knows best how she feels.

2 If you feel you're not getting anywhere, make an appointment to see the consultant, who has the final say about whether your relative can leave hospital.

3 If the consultant insists that your relative is 'too well' to be in hospital, don't feel that it's up to you or other relatives to find alternative care for her if she is not well enough to look after herself. Some people go to the lengths of taking their relative's key away from them so that they cannot be sent home before they are ready or before adequate arrangements for their care have been made.

4 You can refuse to have your relative to stay with you: this might be the only way to force the health or social services to realise that they have to find another solution.

5 If in retrospect you think your relative left hospital much too early, you can complain about it afterwards (see pp 36–39).

FOR MORE INFORMATION

▶ Age Concern England Briefing Paper *Hospital discharge procedures.*

▶ Carers National Association Information Sheet 6 *Hospital discharge.*

▶ Help the Aged Information Sheet 14 *Going into hospital.*

▶ Department of Health circulars LAC(89)7 and HC(89)5, the accompanying booklet *Discharge of Patients from Hospital* and *Hospital Discharge Workbook – A manual on hospital discharge practice.* For copies write to the Department of Health (address on p 82).

▶ Department of Health leaflet HSG(92)4 *Patient's Charter*, available from Christians, 191–195 Southampton Way, London SE5 7EF. Tel: 071-701 0800. Also available from GPs' surgeries, libraries and hospitals.

2 Making plans

Many people find that when they come out of hospital, they are less able to cope than they were before they went in. Some older people may have been only just managing before they went into hospital. Sometimes a bit of help at first can make all the difference, and many people regain their independence quickly. Others find that they continue to need much more help than before. A few people have to rethink their situation completely.

This chapter looks in detail at discharge planning and explains how the hospital staff and other professionals should help you and your relative plan for when she leaves hospital. It also considers some of the temporary arrangements that might be possible if she can't go straight home.

GRAHAM

6 She's lost her old spark. I think her experience that night affected her more deeply than anyone realised at the time. 9

'I had a phone call from Mum at six o'clock one Saturday morning. She sounded very confused and upset. She said she had gone to bed at about ten the night before but had started to feel "strange". She tried ringing me but Gwen and I were out and her next-door neighbour was away too so she dialled 999. The ambulance came very quickly and took her to the accident and emergency department of the local hospital. They checked her over, told her she might have had a very slight stroke, gave her a cup of tea and sent her home, still in her nightie, in a taxi.

'By then it was four in the morning and the house was freezing. The hospital didn't try to ring me although my number was in her handbag, which she took with her in the ambulance. She told me she wandered around in a daze for ages before she managed to sit down and ring me.

'I went over there straight away and found her still in her nightie sitting in a chair. Fortunately, the heating had come on by then. I stayed with her for the rest of the day and that night. By Sunday evening she seemed fine so I came home so that I could go to work the next day.

'I try to call in on her two or three times a week and ring every evening to check she's all right. She seems OK but there is definitely a change in her – she's lost her old spark. I think her experience that night affected her more deeply than anyone realised at the time.'

Who should be involved in discharge planning?

Graham's mother's experience was unsettling and unpleasant. The accident and emergency staff should not have discharged her without finding out whether she needed any support at home. Even though she was admitted to hospital in an emergency, she should still have been involved in planning her own discharge.

Your relative

It should go without saying that the most important person to involve in discussions about her care after hospital is your relative herself. Government guidelines state that patients must be at the centre of the planning process. In some hospitals patients feel really involved, but in others patients never even find out the names of the nurses or sort out who is responsible for what.

If decisions are being made without consulting your relative or she seems unsure about what is happening, she should talk to a doctor or nurse about it. You can do this with her or for her if she wants you to. If she doesn't agree with what has been decided, it is important for her to say so. Older people are often deferential to doctors and nurses, so you might have to encourage your relative to stand up for what she wants (see pp 36–37 for more on this).

You as carer

The second most important person to get involved is you – the carer. If you are caring at home you will have your own needs and opinions and these should be taken into account when any arrangements for your relative's care are being discussed. There is more on this on pages 24 and 35.

It can be difficult to make sure you are consulted, especially if you live some distance from the hospital. Start by finding out the name of the sister in charge of the ward (see p 20) or the named nurse responsible for your relative (see p 21) and ask to speak to her when you first visit or telephone the ward. If you want to talk to her when you next visit, check when she will be available. She may also suggest that you see the hospital social worker (see p 21). Before you visit, prepare a list of specific questions you want to ask and make sure you get answers to them.

You will probably have to telephone the ward regularly in between visits rather than relying on hospital staff to let you know what's happening on a day-to-day basis. However, the Government has said that if your relative wants or needs you to be involved in making decisions about medical or any other kind of care, you should be consulted at every stage and before decisions are made. Your relative should then refuse to agree to anything until you have been consulted.

If you can, make a note of the date of any discussions, what was said and who said it. That way you can chase people if they don't do what they said they would do. And if things go badly wrong you will have a record of what was agreed. It is also a good idea to write a letter summarising what you think has been agreed.

SAYING WHAT YOU THINK

▶ If you are a full-time carer, remember that you are the expert on looking after your relative. Try to sort out in your own mind what services and help you think your relative might need when she leaves hospital. You might have to ask for something specific such as physiotherapy. If you're not sure about what she might need or what's available, get advice from one of the organisations listed on pages 79–88.

▶ If you feel that assumptions are being made about the amount of care you can offer, do not be pressured into agreeing to anything you are not happy with. It's important not to commit yourself to anything that you know won't be manageable.

▶ Take someone with you to give you moral support and to back up what you are saying. One of the organisations listed on pages 53–54 might be able to give you support.

Hospital staff

Different people will be involved in caring for your relative in hospital. Most of them will also be involved in deciding when she can leave hospital and what help she will need, if any.

The person in charge of her medical care is the **consultant**. Under the consultant is a team of doctors and nurses who are in charge of her day-to-day care. The **ward sister** – also known as a **senior sister**, **charge nurse** or **ward manager** – has overall responsibility for the patients on the ward. Below the sister are qualified **staff nurses** and unqualified **student nurses**, **nursing auxiliaries**, **nursing assistants** and **health care support workers**.

Other key staff who may be involved in planning care include:

Physiotherapist To help patients who have pain or difficulty in moving.

Occupational therapist To help patients manage daily tasks and give advice on aids (gadgets and equipment that might help them) and adaptations to the home.

Hospital social worker To give advice and make arrangements for when patients leave hospital.

Community liaison nurse, care nurse organiser or **care co-ordinator** To liaise with the providers of services if the care to be arranged is very complicated.

Rehabilitation officer To co-ordinate the rehabilitation of patients who are going home.

Some of these people may also visit patients at home.

Hospital staff often work in teams so that everyone can meet and discuss a patient's care, but it is obviously easy for things to go wrong when so many people are involved. In hospitals with good discharge standards, each patient has a specific nurse – **a named nurse** – with responsibility for them. He or she should co-ordinate all the different aspects of the patient's care and make sure they know what is happening.

People from outside the hospital

If your relative is going to need any care from outside the hospital, the people who are to provide it should be involved in discussing what is needed. Government guidelines say that it is the hospital's responsibility to liaise with outside organisations while your relative is in hospital. If her care needs are very complex, everyone involved should come into the hospital to discuss with her how she feels and what she needs.

This might happen in a **case conference**. This is a meeting for the person needing care and all the people involved in providing it. It might include someone from social services, a district nurse, or a hospital after-care scheme co-ordinator. Carers are sometimes invited too.

Although a case conference can be a good way of getting everyone together and sorting things out, they may not be easy if you are not used to them, especially if people use a lot of jargon. Try not to be intimidated – if there is something you are not clear about, ask for an explanation. It's up to the professionals to make sure that you and your relative are able to participate fully in the decision-making (see pp 36–37 for more on standing up for yourself). It is better not to agree to anything on the spot; ask for time to think things over.

If your relative has hearing problems or if English is not her first language, the hospital should provide someone who can use sign language or an interpreter who has an understanding of health matters. If they don't have an interpreter, the local Community Relations Council or Council for Racial Equality might be able to provide one (see p 53).

What needs to be discussed?

Before your relative leaves hospital, she will need to think about:

▶ what she will need, if anything, in order to manage;

▶ where she is going to go when she first comes out.

What help does your relative need?

Before your relative leaves hospital, the hospital staff will decide whether she could benefit from any further medical care, for example physiotherapy.

The next step should be to find out whether she will need any other help. As explained on pages 13–14, Government guidelines say that the hospital staff should start to discuss this with her before she is admitted if her admission is planned or as soon as possible after admission if she is admitted unexpectedly.

The help she needs will depend to some extent on why she went into hospital. If she went in for observation or to give you a break from caring, for example, her needs are unlikely to have changed much. But if she has had a heart attack or a stroke, she is likely to need extra help when she leaves.

If she was admitted to hospital either after becoming ill suddenly or as a result of a fall or accident, the hospital staff should try to find out whether there are any underlying problems which caused her to end up in an emergency situation. She may not have been coping well for some time and her admission to hospital could be a sign that she needs more help.

Government guidelines state that patients should only be asked once for all basic personal details and that they should be *given appropriate opportunities* to share further information at all stages of their admission and stay in hospital.

Ideally, time should be set aside for a proper interview. Unfortunately in many wards there is a much more 'hit and miss' approach – your relative might be asked one question in passing one day and another the next, probably by several different people. It might help her to follow what is going on if she knows the kinds of questions to expect.

What help does your relative think she needs?

This seems like an obvious starting point for any discussion about your relative's care, but it is surprising how often people forget to ask this question. Even if she is given an opportunity to say how she feels, she may feel that people are prying or putting pressure on her.

She may not trust them to come to the right conclusions. For example, if she is fearful about having to go into a care home, she may not admit to needing much help. But this may mean that she misses out on essential alternative forms of support such as help at home. She may be reluctant to admit that she can do some things at all in case any help she already receives is withdrawn. But this may mean that she is offered the wrong kind of help.

JACKIE

❝He just refused to leave the hospital unless they could come up with another arrangement.❞

'The hospital staff were very kind to my father after his coronary artery bypass, especially when he was in intensive care. But when he started to get better, there was obviously pressure on them to get him out of the bed so that someone else could have it. He and my brother had been managing quite well on their own for several years, but my brother has cerebral palsy and is in a wheelchair. He can do a limited amount around the house but he couldn't look after my father.

'Someone from social services arranged for a home help to go in twice a week to do the washing and cleaning, and the hospital contacted the community nursing service to arrange for my father to have a district nurse to change his dressing and help him get washed and dressed in the morning. I can get there in the evenings to help put him to bed.

'The day before he left hospital we were told that a district nurse could come every morning between 10.30 and 11. My father has always hated being in bed and he was very distressed that he might have to wait most of the morning before he could get up. He's a strong-minded man and he just refused to leave the hospital unless they could come up with another arrangement. He said he would rather die now than spend the rest of his life in bed.

'The staff nurse was quite taken aback at first – so was I – but she could see how depressed he was going to get if something wasn't done about it. She phoned the district nurses manager and eventually they said that if he didn't mind getting up very early, a district nurse could call before she did her other visits rather than afterwards.'

But not everyone is as assertive as Jackie's father. Some people have special needs but feel uncomfortable about talking about them. A Muslim person, for example, may need special help if their right hand has been paralysed by a stroke as it is Muslim custom to use only the left hand for toilet hygiene. The hospital staff may not be sensitive to this kind of difficulty.

Help your relative draw up a list of the help she feels she needs. If she needs your help in putting her point of view, arrange a time when you can be there too.

What help do you think she needs?

The hospital staff should also want to find out what help you think your relative needs. They shouldn't assume that you will share her views. For example, she may say that you can look after her without any outside help, but you may disagree. Women are often expected to look after a relative as part of their normal 'duties', whereas men might be offered more support. If you want to discuss how you feel separately, you can ask to see someone on your own.

If you are – or are about to become – a full-time carer, the hospital staff should ask you about your own state of health and how you feel about caring. If you are contemplating caring full-time for the first time, make sure you discuss this with them before you commit yourself. There may be other options you haven't thought of. If you are already caring full-time, this might be the moment when you have to say you can't go on. Or you might feel that you could continue if you had some extra help, such as one day off a week while your relative goes to a day centre.

What medical help does she need?

Does your relative need to take medicines or change dressings and can she manage to do this on her own? Does she need injections? Does she have any mental health problems? Is she incontinent? Does she need full-time nursing?

NOTE All medical decisions should be made on the basis of your relative's health alone, taking no account of other considerations such as how much money she has or how much help her family can provide. If you or your relative suspects that medical decisions are being made for the wrong reasons, you should complain. Contact Age Concern England or the Carers National Association (addresses on pp 89 and 81) for advice on this. For more on how to complain see pages 36–39.

How well can she manage at home?

The hospital staff should find out whether your relative can look after herself. For example, can she get in and out of a bed and chair, get washed and dressed, eat her meals, go to the toilet? Can she do the housework, washing, cooking and shopping? She may have to demonstrate that she can perform these tasks before she is discharged.

Some people are offered a **home visit** with an occupational therapist to see how they will manage at home and to find out whether equipment or adaptations are needed. A hospital social worker or someone from social services might go too if the care required is very complex or if you are going to need a lot of help to continue caring. Patients are not discharged during a home visit – they return to the hospital first.

What help is she getting already?

Does she live alone or with someone to care for her? Does she have family nearby to support her? What help can she expect from friends and neighbours? Does she already get any help from the health or social services or voluntary organisations? Does she pay privately for any help? Is she happy with the help she is getting? Is it still the kind of help she needs?

Is her home still suited to her needs?

Does her home need to be repaired, improved or adapted in any way? For example, can she get up and down steps and stairs? Can she use the toilet, bathroom and kitchen without difficulty? Is her home warm and dry?

Does she need any equipment?

Does she need any equipment to aid mobility such as a wheelchair, zimmer frame, crutches or walking sticks? Does she need a telephone or a home alarm? Are there any other gadgets or aids which would help her?

Can she get about outside?

Can she get to the shops and the doctor and to visit friends and family? Is there any public transport? Can she use it? If not, what help does she need with getting about?

Is she at risk?

If she is unsteady on her feet, is she likely to have a fall? If she has epilepsy, diabetes or a weak heart, could she collapse suddenly? If she is suffering from dementia, could she put herself or others at risk, for example by forgetting she has turned an appliance on or leaving the front door open? Is she likely to wander off at night or to let a stranger into her home?

If you're not happy

Getting help can sometimes be difficult because it is not always clear who is responsible for what. For example, the hospital might think it is the responsibility of social services to arrange convalescent care for your relative in a nursing home but social services might think it is the hospital's responsibility. This can be unsettling for patients, who may have to wait to find out what is going to happen to them while the negotiations go on. If this happens, get advice from one of the organisations listed on pages 53–54. Health and local authorities must have agreements in place to provide appropriate services and care. See page 16 for more on this.

NOTE Your relative does not have to accept any help when she comes out of hospital even if she is offered it. She may feel that she will receive enough support from friends, family and neighbours. If so, try to ensure that everyone understands what they are agreeing to do and that too much of the burden of caring does not fall on you or one or two others.

Where to next?

The discharge planning process may also need to include a discussion about where your relative goes when she first leaves hospital. She may be able to go straight home, or she may need to stay somewhere temporarily or have a period of convalescence until she is well or mobile enough to go home, perhaps with extra help.

Going straight home

If your relative is going straight home, she will need to think carefully about whether she needs any help to carry on living there. You and other family, friends and neighbours might be able to give all the help she needs. If not, the health and social services might be able to provide it or she might be able to pay for help herself. Chapter 3 explains the different kinds of help that might be available and who might provide it.

If your relative lives alone, she might feel uneasy and lonely after the security and companionship of the hospital ward. You could:

▶ arrange a rota of relatives or friends who can visit or stay the night;

▶ contact a hospital aftercare scheme (see p 51) or a local voluntary organisation or neighbourhood scheme to see if they can send a volunteer to visit (see p 50);

▶ find out if there is a sitting service in the area (see p 56);

▶ investigate how much it would cost to pay for an agency companion (see pp 52–53);

▶ have a home alarm installed (see p 58).

If you and your relative live together, think carefully about whether you can look after her at home, especially if she needs full-time care.

WINSTON 'I've been looking after my mother for ten years now. She's got chronic arthritis and for the last five years she's had Parkinson's disease as well so I had to take early retirement to look after her full-time. She's gone into hospital for two weeks to give me a break. She comes home in two days' time but I don't know whether I can carry on any longer. I just feel so tired.'

If you are not in good health yourself, your partner may have been caring for you until now and you will be facing the difficult prospect of a complete role reversal.

Don't feel guilty if you feel you can't cope with caring. If you keep going, you may end up being ill yourself and then both of you will need looking after. If you feel you can't manage even with extra help, your relative might have to consider a residential or nursing home.

FOR MORE INFORMATION

▶ Age Concern England Factsheet 29 *Finding residential and nursing home accommodation.*

▶ *Caring in a Crisis: Finding and paying for residential and nursing home care,* published by ACE Books (details on p 90).

Staying with you temporarily

If your relative lives alone and can't manage at home when she first comes out of hospital, one option might be for her to stay with you or another relative or friend for a few weeks. This might give her the strength and confidence she needs to go back to her own home.

DINAH 'Pat lives in the flat above mine. She's a very independent person and drives her own car. Two weeks ago she tripped over and somehow managed to break her hip. She can just about walk with crutches now but she's lost all her confidence and she says she doesn't want to leave the hospital. It's not like her at all. I've offered to have her to stay with me for a few weeks until she feels able to be on her own again.'

If you do offer to have your relative to stay with you temporarily, make sure you both agree on the short-term nature of the arrangement.

Otherwise you may end up inadvertently becoming a permanent carer. Even if you don't mind doing this, it's better to have made a conscious decision to do so.

Before you decide, think about:

▶ whether you can manage to look after your relative;

▶ whether you will need any help;

▶ whether you will have to rearrange or adapt your home, for example by using a downstairs room as a bedroom;

▶ how any other members of the family will feel – you will need their support.

Try not to feel pressured by your relative or the hospital staff into offering to have her to stay with you if you don't think it will work. Perhaps she could convalesce in a residential or nursing home (see below), or there might be someone else who could have her to stay for a while.

Convalescent care

If your relative is not able or ready to look after herself when she first comes out of hospital and can't stay with you or anyone else, the local authority might offer her two or three weeks' convalescence in a residential or nursing home, although she may have to pay towards the cost. For stays of up to eight weeks, the local authority can charge her what appears 'reasonable' for her to pay; it doesn't have to carry out a means test to determine how much she can afford.

If your relative is not offered convalescent care by the local authority, you can still ask for it. If it is refused, you or your relative might be able to pay for it yourselves. It might be money well spent if it enables her to live at home afterwards.

JANE 'Going into a convalescent home for two weeks made all the difference to Mum after her cataract operation. My sisters and I talked about it with her and we were all so pushed with our own families and jobs we decided to club together and pay for it. We felt a bit guilty about not going down to stay with her but she really enjoyed it – the home was comfortable and they looked after her very well. I went to stay with her for a few days when she first went home, but she was able to do most things for herself by then and was wanting to look after me instead of the other way round!'

Getting something in writing

If it has been decided that your relative will need further services or help once she has been discharged, she or you should ask for a written summary of what has been agreed. In its guidelines on hospital discharge, the Government has said that *'important points about a patient's discharge should be confirmed in writing before the patient leaves the hospital'*, including, if appropriate, information about:

▶ medication;

▶ lifestyle;

▶ diet;

▶ symptoms to watch for;

▶ where to get help if it is needed;

▶ arrangements for any day care;

▶ arrangements for outpatient appointments.

The Government recommends that patients should be provided with this information in the form of *their own copy of an agreed discharge plan*. The following is an example of a good discharge plan:

WHAT YOU NEED TO KNOW WHEN YOU LEAVE HOSPITAL

Patient's name

Patient's address

Hospital telephone number

Hospital address

Date of admission

Date of discharge

Name and number of ward

GP's name and telephone number

While you were in hospital your consultant was

You were also seen by Dr

and by

The senior nurse on the ward was

Your named nurse was

You were in hospital because

You had the following treatment

As a result you need to know

The medicines you are taking home are

Special information you need to know about your medicines

We will be lending you the following equipment

You will be taking home the following dressings

These services have been arranged when you go home:

	Date	*Transport*
Outpatient appointment **Telephone:**		
Day hospital **Telephone:**		
Day centre **Telephone:**		
Visit from district nurse **Telephone:**		
Visit from social services **Telephone:**		

Home care services
Telephone:

Meals on wheels
Telephone:

Physiotherapy
Telephone:

Assessing your relative's needs

Under the NHS and Community Care Act 1990 local authorities *must* assess the needs of people who appear to need **community care services**. Community care services include social services such as home care, day care, the provision of aids, and residential or nursing home care which are the responsibility of the local authority either to provide or arrange provision. There is more on the services which your relative might be able to receive and who might provide them in Chapter 3.

LOCAL AUTHORITY

When we use the words 'local authority' or 'council' in this book, we mean whichever of the following applies to you:

▶   a county (such as Shropshire or Devon);

▶   a metropolitan borough (or district – such as Sandwell or Tameside);

▶   a London borough (such as Haringey or Sutton);

▶   the City of London.

The structure of local government is currently being reviewed. Some county and shire district councils may be merged into single authorities. The review is due to be completed by the end of 1994 and any changes should be implemented by April 1997.

What is an assessment?

If your relative may need community care services when she goes home, someone – usually a hospital social worker or someone from the local social services department – should carry out an assessment of her needs while she is in hospital. This person may be called a **care**

manager (see p 48). The assessment might be based partly or completely on any discussions that the hospital staff have already had with her.

After the assessment, the local authority will decide whether it can arrange or provide the services she has been assessed as needing. Some local authorities do not have enough money to provide all the services that are needed. This means that your relative may not get all the help she needs even if she has been assessed as needing it. In some circumstances, however, the local authority has a statutory duty to – that is, it *must* – provide services (see pp 46–47).

There is no set national pattern to the way assessments are done. The way they are handled varies from one local authority to another. All local authorities must, however, provide written information about their procedures, including details of:

▶ who can have an assessment;

▶ how and where to apply for an assessment;

▶ how it is decided what services should be provided;

▶ how to complain.

You should be able to obtain this information from the hospital, the local authority or a Citizens Advice Bureau. There may also be copies in libraries and GPs' surgeries.

NOTE If the local authority seems to be refusing to make a community care assessment of your relative because it thinks she can afford to pay privately, you should complain (see pp 38–39). The Department of Health has said that *'the provision of services should not be related to the ability of the user or their families to meet the costs'*.

If your relative's needs are very complex, several people might be involved in the assessment, for example a social worker and an occupational therapist. This is called a **multidisciplinary assessment**. If she had an assessment before she went into hospital, she may need to be **reassessed** to decide whether she now needs any different or extra help.

If you or your relative thinks she needs or is entitled to an assessment but she hasn't been offered one, ask to see the hospital social worker or contact the social services department directly. The telephone number of the local social services department will be listed in the telephone book under the name of the local authority. Ask to speak to the **duty officer**, who should put you on to the right person or tell you who to contact. This may well be the **team leader** or **service manager** for the area where your relative lives (see pp 48–49 for more on how social services departments are organised).

If your relative is disabled

If your relative is disabled, she can ask for her needs to be assessed under the Disabled Persons (Services, Consultation and Representation) Act 1986. In this case the local authority must provide her with the services she has been assessed as needing under the Chronically Sick and Disabled Persons (CSDP) Act 1970. She has a right to services under the CSDP Act if she is:

▶ substantially or permanently handicapped;

▶ blind or partially sighted;

▶ deaf or hard of hearing;

▶ mentally ill;

▶ mentally handicapped.

Older people applying for help because of mental disorder, chronic illness or disability – such as arthritis, effects of stroke, loss of sight or hearing – should ask to be assessed as 'disabled'. Under the Disabled Persons Act, the local authority must assess a disabled person's needs if asked to do so by their carer.

If during an assessment a person is found to be disabled, the local authority must assess that person for their needs under the Disabled Persons Act at the same time as it assesses their need for community care services under the NHS and Community Care Act.

What happens during an assessment?

The kinds of questions your relative will be asked during the assessment will be similar to those listed on pages 23–26. A good assessment will be concerned with her psychological and social needs as well as her physical needs. Again, your relative should be central to the assessment process so that her needs can be identified as closely as possible and the person carrying out the assessment can help her consider all the options that are open to her.

Carers are entitled to be consulted and to be involved in the assessment. Your relative's permission would need to be sought, however, to divulge any information she might have given in confidence to the assessor. If your relative is disabled they must take into account your ability to continue to provide care on a regular basis. If you need help to continue caring or if you and your relative don't agree about what she needs, you can be assessed in your own right. You can ask for a separate assessment if you want one.

Your relative may be given a written record of the discussions that have taken place; if you ask you should get one. This may be in the form of a **care plan** (see p 47). You or your relative could also make a note of the discussions. You then have something to refer to if anything goes wrong. You might want to write a letter confirming what you think has been agreed.

NOTE Your relative has the right to see local authority records about herself, including the details of her assessment. You don't have the right to see anyone else's records so you can't ask to see her records on her behalf. The local authority should have a set procedure for showing people their records; they may charge a fee for providing copies of records.

If at any point you and your relative feel you are getting lost in the assessment process, ask the person making the assessment to explain what is happening. Or you could contact a Citizens Advice Bureau or Age Concern England or the Carers National Association (addresses on pp 89 and 81).

FOR MORE INFORMATION

▶ Age Concern England Briefing Paper *Local authority assessments for community care services*.

▶ Age Concern England Factsheet 32 *Disability and ageing: Your rights to social services*.

▶ Counsel and Care Factsheet 18 *Community care services for older people*.

▶ Carers National Association Information Sheet 1 *NHS and Community Care Act – What it means for carers*.

▶ *The Community Care Handbook: The new system explained*, published by ACE Books (details on p 91).

How to complain

Although there are Government guidelines on discharge planning (see pp 11–12), standards vary from hospital to hospital and even from ward to ward within a hospital. So what we have described in this chapter is what *should* happen. This may be completely different from what your relative experiences. If, when you have read this chapter, you feel her discharge is going badly wrong, try to complain before she leaves hospital. Once she has left, it will probably be much more difficult to sort things out.

Many people are reluctant to complain about the care they or their relatives receive. They may worry that they will be branded as troublemakers and receive worse, not better, care. But if you or your relative is unhappy with the care she receives, it's important that you don't just accept it. The tips on standing up for yourself in the box below might help.

STANDING UP FOR YOURSELF

▶ Find out the names of the people you will be dealing with, otherwise you will be at a disadvantage.

▶ Work out beforehand what you are going to say – practise if it helps you get it clear in your mind, or discuss the points you want to make with someone else.

▶ Make a list of the main points you want to get across – in your mind at least. If you write your list down take it with you so that you don't forget anything.

▶ Try to be specific – say exactly what you think and what you want to happen, making reference to the Government guidelines if this is helpful.

▶ Try to *seem* confident even if you don't *feel* it. If you can feel yourself getting uptight or anxious, breathe deeply and speak more slowly.

▶ Stay calm. Even if you are in a heated discussion try not to get angry or aggressive.

▶ Keep to the point – try not to be diverted by side issues.

▶ Be persistent. Keep repeating your message until someone listens to you.

- ▶ Make it clear that you are not going to give up. Many organisations work on the principle that most people will give up eventually.
- ▶ Say 'No' if you mean 'No'. Don't be persuaded into agreeing to something you are not happy with.
- ▶ Listen – remember that your point of view isn't the only one, but don't lose sight of what you want to achieve in the end.
- ▶ Remember you have the right to be heard: the services belong to you.

Complaining about the hospital

If you or your relative wants to complain about the hospital:

1   If the proposed discharge is imminent, phone to make an urgent appointment with the General Manager of the hospital, or the Chief Executive if it's a Trust hospital. You may need to formally complain in writing following this if the matter is not resolved. The Community Health Council (see p 53) might be able to help you write to the hospital and may be able to provide advice and information on NHS complaints systems.

2   Discuss the problem with the ward sister and/or consultant. If important matters are discussed, write afterwards to confirm what was said on both sides or ask them to do so.

3   If you are not satisfied with the hospital's response to the formal complaint, you can ask the Health Service Ombudsman (address on p 83) to investigate your relative's case. You should telephone first and they will send you a booklet explaining the procedure. You must give the hospital a chance to investigate the matter before you contact the Ombudsman. Complaints procedures can be lengthy so you may want to seek advice from the Community Health Council about the different procedures.

SCOTLAND AND NORTHERN IRELAND
- ▶ In Scotland, Community Health Councils are called Local Health Councils.
- ▶ In Northern Ireland, they are called District Committees for Health and Personal Social Services.

▶ In Northern Ireland, complaints about health and social services are dealt with by the Parliamentary Commissioner of Administration and Commissioner for Complaints.

Complaining about the social services department

You might want to complain about the social services department because you are unhappy with the outcome of an assessment or with the way an assessment was carried out. Every local authority has to have a complaints procedure. If you or your relative wants to make a complaint:

1   Start by trying to sort out the problem informally with the person you have been dealing with or their line manager.

2   If you don't get anywhere, ask them for information on how to make a formal complaint or ring the council and ask to speak to the person designated to deal with complaints. All local authorities must have a formal complaints procedure which is explained to you. Or you could write to the Director of Social Services and say you want to complain. You should receive a response to your complaint within 28 days; or you should be contacted within 28 days and have a full response within 3 months.

3   If, after you have complained, you are still not satisfied with the outcome, you can have the matter put before a review panel if you ask for this in writing within 28 days. The panel must have at least one member who is not involved with the local authority. This panel will consider the evidence and state its views in writing to both you and the authority within 28 days. You should be informed in writing at least 10 days beforehand about the review panel meeting, which you can attend. The local authority then has 28 days to give you a decision in writing, stating the reasons for the decision and any action to be taken.

4   If you have gone through the formal complaints procedure but still want to take the matter further, you can contact the Local Government Ombudsman, who looks into cases of maladministration by local authorities that cause injustice. You must complain within 12 months. For more information contact your local council or Citizens Advice Bureau or phone the Local Government Ombudsman (address on p 85).

For support in making a formal complaint, you could contact a local councillor (you can find out who the local councillors are by ringing the local town hall or civic centre – look in the phone book under the name of the local council) or the local Member of Parliament (you can find details in the front of the phone book).

Where to get help and advice

▶ You can get help and advice about making a complaint from the organisations listed on pages 53–54. In particular, RADAR (address on p 87) can explain all the various forms of complaint in more detail.

▶ If you are making a complaint about the health services, you could also contact your local Community Health Council, the Patients' Association or Home from Hospital (addresses on pp 87 and 84).

▶ In some areas there is also a carers' support officer based in the District Health Authority and/or the local authority. Ask the Citizens Advice Bureau if there is one locally.

FOR MORE INFORMATION

▶ Age Concern England Factsheet 32 *Disability and ageing: Your rights to social services.*

▶ Carers National Association Information Sheet 7 *Complaining about health, social services and social work departments.*

▶ *Complaint about the Council? How to complain to the Local Government Ombudsman*, available from local councils, Citizens Advice Bureaux or the Local Government Ombudsman (address on p 85).

3 Getting help

Many older people manage on their own or with the help of family, friends and neighbours when they go home from hospital. For others, help from the health and social services, voluntary organisations and private agencies is essential. Finding out exactly what is on offer and who can provide it is not always easy. Ideally, the hospital staff should help your relative sort this out, but in practice this does not always happen.

This chapter describes the help your relative might be able to get from the health service and the social services department. It also looks at the role played by charities and voluntary organisations, hospital aftercare schemes and private agencies. There is a chart on pages 54–56 showing the main types of help available and whom to contact for them. Finally, it looks at aids and adaptations to make your relative's home safer or easier for her to live in.

TREVOR

❝I was a bit sceptical at first but they really got their act together. She should have been given this kind of help long ago.❞

'My aunt was in hospital for three weeks after she slipped on her hall floor and broke her collarbone. She's 85 and she's got arthritis in both hands and in one knee. She's also got a large cyst on the back of her other knee so walking is very painful and difficult for her. She was very concerned about going home again – so was I – but she didn't want to involve social services because she was worried they would put her in a home. I can only help out at weekends because I work full-time and I can't take much time off work. She's a widow and hasn't got any children.

'The charge nurse was very reassuring. She arranged a meeting at the hospital to talk about how she was going to cope and what help she could get. My aunt was there of course and so was the charge nurse. They had also asked the hospital social worker, an occupational therapist, a physiotherapist, a district nurse, a home care organiser and someone from the hospital aftercare scheme.

'I must admit I was a bit sceptical at first but they really got their act together. She should have been given this kind of help long ago. Now a home help comes twice a day weekdays and in the mornings at the weekend. She makes the bed, does the cleaning and washing and empties the commode. She came round the day my aunt got home from hospital, which was nice. As well as the home help, someone from the hospital aftercare scheme has been coming three days a week in the afternoon to make a cup of tea and get her a snack for the evening.

'She gets meals on wheels for lunch every day and they've organised a special menu for her as she's diabetic. Every Monday and Thursday she goes to a day hospital – they come and pick her up and drop her off again. The occupational therapist organised a high back chair for her and last week the hospital social worker sent someone round to put a new carpet at the bottom of the stairs where she had slipped.'

The community health services

After your relative has been discharged, she might have to return to the hospital for outpatient appointments, a day clinic or another inpatient stay. She might also receive home visits from some hospital-based staff such as a physiotherapist or speech therapist. But most of her health care will probably be provided by health professionals based in the community. The main people your relative might see are listed below, together with the kind of help they can provide.

HEALTH AUTHORITIES

▶ In England and Wales, the Regional Health Authority (RHA) is responsible for providing health care to people living in that region.

▶ The District Health Authority (DHA) is responsible for purchasing secondary health care (mainly hospitals) in the district. You can find their number in the phone book under the name of the health authority or in the *Yellow Pages* under 'Health Authorities and Services'. Residents who are the patients of GP fundholders (see below) have these services purchased by their GP.

▶ The Family Health Services Authority (FHSA) is responsible for purchasing primary health care (GPs, dentists, district nurses, etc). You can find their number in the phone book. It is expected that DHAs and FHSAs will merge to form single authorities.

▶ Trusts are independent organisations within the NHS which have contracts to run certain health care services.

▶ In Scotland, health services are purchased by health boards and mainly provided at a local level by trusts.

▶ In Northern Ireland, health services are purchased by four area health and social services boards and provided at a local level by trusts and units of management.

General practitioner (GP)

Most people receive health care from a family doctor or general practitioner (GP) who works in a surgery, health centre or clinic. The GP is a key person for your relative because she or he can arrange many other types of community health care.

If your relative is staying with you, she can register as a temporary resident with a local GP for up to three months and still remain registered with her own GP. During that time she will be entitled to the same treatment as a permanent resident, provided the GP thinks she needs it.

Some GPs now control their own budgets to buy care for their patients; they are called **GP fundholders**.

District nurse

District nurses are community nurses who nurse people at home. A district nurse might visit your relative when she comes out of hospital to change dressings, give injections, help with bathing and toileting, lifting and turning.

District nurses may be able to arrange for equipment such as a commode, bedpan or special mattress to be provided. They can also give you advice on lifting and turning your relative, preventing pressure (bed) sores and dealing with incontinence.

The hospital may arrange for your relative to be visited by a district nurse or her GP may do this after she has left hospital. Where it is clear that someone will need district nurse support after discharge from hospital, this should be arranged *before* she is discharged.

Health visitor

Health visitors are community nurses who have had extra training in working with people at home. They can provide advice and information not only about health matters but also about local services and State benefits. They can also suggest practical ways of coping with day-to-day problems and liaise between people at home and social services. Your relative's GP should arrange for a visit from a health visitor if she needs one.

Physiotherapist

A physiotherapist might visit your relative if she needs help with mobility or pain relief or breathing exercises. A physiotherapist can also organise walking equipment such as sticks, a walking (zimmer) frame or possibly a wheelchair. If you are caring full-time, she or he can give you advice on how to lift and turn your relative.

The hospital or GP should be able to organise home visits from a physiotherapist. In some areas the community physiotherapy service is limited, but some hospital-based physiotherapists visit people at home. See Age Concern England's leaflet *Physiotherapy and older people.*

Community psychiatric nurse

A community psychiatric nurse (CPN) helps people with mental health problems who live at home. If you are caring full-time and your relative's behaviour is very difficult, a CPN may also be able to give you advice and support.

DAPHNE 'The CPN has been a real friend. Sometimes I've just needed to talk to her about how I feel when my mother's so aggressive and nasty to me.'

Not all areas have community psychiatric nurses – ask the GP whether there are any in the area.

Speech therapist

Speech therapists help people who have speech disorders or who have lost their speech, perhaps after a stroke. Not all areas have community speech therapists, but some hospital-based speech therapists visit people at home. Ask the GP what's available in the area.

Continence adviser/stoma care adviser

If your relative is incontinent (unable to control her bladder or bowel or both), a continence adviser may visit her at home. She or he may treat the problem, give advice on how to cope with continence problems that cannot be cured, or provide information about products such as incontinence pads. Ask the GP or district nurse, or phone the Incontinence Information Helpline on 091-213 0050 for the name of your nearest continence adviser.

If your relative has had a colostomy or ileostomy (an operation to remove part of the bowel), there may be a stoma care adviser in the area who can give advice on using a colostomy bag. Ask the GP for details.

Link worker/interpreter

In some areas there is a link worker and/or an interpreter to work with people whose first language is not English. The GP should know what is available locally.

Chiropodist, dentist and optician

Chiropody (care of the feet) is free to all senior citizens. To find out more about chiropody services phone the District Health Authority or ask the GP. To find out which dentists and opticians might make home visits phone the Family Health Services Authority.

FOR MORE INFORMATION

▶ Age Concern England Factsheet 5 *Dental care in retirement*.

▶ *Your Rights*, published annually by ACE Books (details on p 91).

Macmillan nurse/Marie Curie nurse

If your relative has cancer, she may be able to have home visits from a Macmillan nurse or a Marie Curie nurse, who are specially trained to give extra nursing help and counselling to people with cancer and their families. The hospital or your relative's GP or district nurse might arrange this, or you can contact the Cancer Relief Macmillan Fund or Marie Curie Cancer Care (addresses on pp 80 and 85).

If you're not happy

In some areas the health services are overstretched – you and your relative might have to push to get what she is entitled to. If she is still in hospital and it looks as though she won't get the health care she needs once she gets home, she can refuse to be discharged (see p 16). If she is already home and she or you feel she is not getting the health care she needs, start by talking to her GP or district nurse. They may be able to arrange additional help. If you feel you're not getting anywhere, you can complain to the District Health Authority or the FHSA – see pages 36–39 for more on how to complain. Seek advice from the Community Health Council, as arrangements for making complaints vary.

Social services and other sources of help at home

Social services

In England and Wales, the local authority is responsible for providing social services. You can find the number of the social services department in the phone book under the name of the local authority. In Scotland, social services are managed by the local regional council and the social services department is called the social work department. In Northern Ireland, social services are managed by the Personal Social Services Board.

Social services range from meals on wheels to full-time care in a residential or nursing home. Some of these services must be provided by the local authority by law and others may be provided. For full details see Age Concern England Factsheet 32 *Disability and ageing: Your rights to social services.*

Services which must be provided

If your relative is chronically sick or disabled, certain social services must be provided under the Chronically Sick and Disabled Persons (CSDP) Act 1970 and the Disabled Persons Act 1986 if the local authority is satisfied that they are necessary to meet her needs. (See pp 33–34 for a definition of disability.) The services which they must provide are:

▶ practical assistance within the home;

▶ disability aids and equipment;

▶ assistance with adaptations to the home;

▶ provision of meals at home or elsewhere;

▶ provision of, or assistance in, getting a telephone or any special equipment necessary to use a telephone;

▶ provision of, or assistance in, taking advantage of educational or recreational facilities both inside and outside the home, including provision of, or assistance with, transport to and from the facilities;

▶ provision of holidays.

Your relative does not need to be registered as disabled to have the right to receive these services under these Acts.

By law, local authorities must also provide training and occupational facilities in a centre or at home and social work support for people suffering from mental disorder.

Services which may be provided

There are also services which a local authority has the power to provide but does not legally have to provide. Even if your relative is assessed as needing these services (see pp 32–35), she may not receive them. The services may not be available in her area or the local authority may be so overstretched that it cannot afford to provide them. Certain kinds of help may only be given in what the local authority regards as high priority cases. This means that although your relative may be in need of help, others who are in greater need will come first. If she is unhappy with a decision, ask to see the 'eligibility criteria' and consider making a complaint (see pp 38–39). But if a decision is made that your relative does need a service but there is no money available to provide it, there is no right of appeal.

Packages of care and care plans

If your relative needs a range of services, a **package of care** might be arranged for her. An example of a package of care would be help with housework and shopping, a sitting service and help with getting dressed. Some people have a **care plan** which summarises the care they are to receive and who is to provide it.

A care plan should make provision for monitoring the situation and reviewing the assessment regularly. If the situation changes in any way at a later date, the services detailed in the care plan should be adjusted. In some cases it may be necessary to make a new assessment.

Paying for services

If your relative is assessed as needing services she may be asked to contribute towards some or all of them. The local authority can make a charge providing this is 'reasonable'. In assessing your relative's ability to pay, it should take into account her overall financial circumstances, particularly all extra expenditure that may be incurred because of her disability or frailty. All types of income can be taken into account except the Mobility Component of the Disabled Living Allowance. Your resources, or those of your family, should not be taken into account.

All local authorities have their own system of charging. If your relative is asked to make a contribution and feels she can't afford it, she can make representations to the local authority. The law says that if a person 'satisfies' the local authority providing the service that she or he has insufficient means, 'the authority shall not require him to pay more than it appears it is reasonably practical for him to pay'.

How social services departments are organised

Social services departments are organised in different ways across the country, but most have a head office and a number of areas or districts. In each area or district there may be teams covering local communities. These are usually called **neighbourhood, community, locality, patch** or **area teams**. It will usually be the local team that arranges care services for your relative.

Local teams will usually have a **team leader** or **service manager**, a number of **social workers**, and staff who are not fully qualified social workers such as **social work assistants**. Some social workers are based in hospitals and are therefore called **hospital social workers**. An occupational therapist, a home care organiser and a welfare rights unit may also be attached to the team.

Care manager

Care managers are key people in organising social services. A care manager might be a social worker, an occupational therapist, a community psychiatric nurse or another type of professional, depending on what a person's main needs are. Care managers arrange and co-ordinate services, give advice, support and information, and put people in touch with other sources of help, such as local voluntary and self-help groups.

MARY 'The care manager has been very good. A few weeks ago my sister had an important hospital appointment and I couldn't take her because I was going to a funeral. I rang her care manager and explained the problem and within half an hour she'd arranged for an agency nurse to do it. All I had to do was organise a taxi for them.'

Home care team

The most important social service for many older people and their carers is home care. Home care is usually managed on a day-to-day basis by a **home care manager** or **home care organiser** and is provided by **home care workers** or **home care assistants**, who help with tasks like housework and shopping (they used to be called home helps). Some home care assistants help with personal care such as washing and dressing (they may be called **personal care assistants** or **personal care aides**). In some areas, home care is now mainly concerned with personal care tasks and help with housework and shopping may be arranged by the social services department through a voluntary or private organisation.

Occupational therapist

An occupational therapist (OT) may be able to visit your relative at home to teach her how to manage any daily tasks such as washing and dressing that she finds difficult. An OT can also give advice on aids and adaptations for people with a physical disability or mental disorder or illness (see p 57) and may be able to arrange for some of these to be provided. OTs are based in hospitals as well as in the community.

Welfare rights worker

Some social services departments have welfare rights workers who can advise on State benefits and other types of help. They may be based in a welfare rights unit.

FOR MORE INFORMATION

▶ Age Concern Factsheet 6 *Finding help at home.*

▶ Age Concern Factsheet 32 *Disability and ageing: Your rights to social services.*

▶ Counsel and Care Factsheet 9 *Help at home.*

▶ *The Community Care Handbook: The new system explained,* published by ACE Books (details on p 91).

Charities and voluntary organisations

Charities and voluntary organisations may provide:

▶ practical advice and information – some have telephone helplines;

▶ financial help including loans and grants;

▶ neighbourhood schemes – people to visit and help out;

▶ counselling or befriending;

▶ transport.

Voluntary organisations are sometimes contracted to provide services on behalf of the local authority.

Some organisations are concerned with particular health problems, such as the Stroke Association. Many national organisations also have local branches or self-help groups where you can meet other people in a similar situation to your own. For example, it might be helpful to join a local carers' group where you can meet other carers.

SALLY 'My father-in-law goes to a day centre once a week and I spend half my precious day off at the local carers' group. That's how important it is to me. I'd have gone mad without it. No one else really understands how I feel.'

To find out more, contact the national organisation, the Self-Help Centre (address on p 87) or a local Volunteer Bureau or Council for Voluntary Service (contact the National Association of Councils for Voluntary Service – address on p 86).

FOR MORE INFORMATION

▶ Counsel and Care Factsheet 8 *Which charity?*

▶ Help the Aged Information Sheet 6 *Benevolent societies.*

▶ Directory of Social Change publication *A Guide to Grants for Individuals in Need*, edited by David Casson and Paul Brown.

▶ **The Association of Charity Officers** (address on p 80) has over 240 member funds, including some which run residential and nursing homes.

▶ **Charity Search** (address on p 81) is a free service to help you match what you need with an appropriate charity.

Hospital aftercare schemes

For some people, help from a hospital aftercare scheme can make all the difference when they go home from hospital. Volunteers can give all kinds of help, usually for the first few days or weeks – accompanying people home from hospital, visiting them for a chat, helping with shopping or housework, and making sure they get the other help they need.

JANE

❝ I just kept wondering what would have happened if I hadn't been around. ❞

'I'm a hospital aftercare scheme volunteer. I first heard about Mr Cooke on Sunday evening. The staff nurse on duty in the accident and emergency department at the general hospital telephoned me to see if I could "pop in" on a man who had gone in that afternoon complaining of back pain. The doctor had examined him, said he'd strained a muscle badly, prescribed some painkillers, and sent him home that evening, even though he was unable to walk or bend and was still in great pain. He had not been offered any transport home so he had paid for his own taxi.

'I rang him first thing on Monday morning and arranged to call in that morning. I was amazed to find that Mr Cooke, who is 83 and suffers from arthritis, is the main carer for his 84-year-old wife, who has emphysema and a heart condition which means that she has to use an oxygen machine for 12 hours out of 24. She walks with two sticks indoors and has a wheelchair in which she does the shopping for both of them. She has difficulty getting up and down stairs so she uses a chemical toilet which is kept downstairs and which Mr Cooke has to empty every three days. Their daughter lives in Northern Ireland and can only visit occasionally although she telephones them regularly.

'On Wednesday the couple's GP visited at their request. She ordered complete bed rest for Mr Cooke. This meant that his wife had to switch to caring for her husband, taking meals upstairs on a tray to him. Each time she had to have a rest before she could get down the stairs again.

'I visited them again on Thursday and they seemed very weary and depressed. Mr Cooke was still in bed in a lot of pain and Mrs Cooke had not been able to do any housework or deal with the chemical toilet. I rang the hospital but was told by the hospital social worker that he couldn't help because Mr Cooke had been an accident and emergency patient and had never been admitted to the hospital. He suggested I rang social services. The duty social worker said someone would ring Mr and Mrs Cooke the next day to arrange to visit them and assess the situation.

'I went again late on Friday afternoon but they hadn't heard from social services. When I rang social services I was told that so many social workers were off sick that Mr and Mrs Cooke could not be visited for five days. When I insisted, they said they would try to arrange for an emergency home care assistant to call on Saturday and Sunday. No home care assistant turned up, and in desperation Mr and Mrs Cooke rang an agency and paid for some private help which they couldn't really afford. Finally, ten days after Mr Cooke had gone to the hospital, a social worker visited to assess the couple's needs and arranged for a home care assistant to visit every day.

'They were very grateful for the help I was able to give them but I just kept wondering what would have happened if I hadn't been around.'

FOR MORE INFORMATION

▶ **Age Concern England** and the **British Red Cross** (addresses on pp 89 and 80) run hospital aftercare schemes around the country.

Getting private help

If your relative can afford to, she may prefer to arrange the help she needs privately. For example, she may not want the kinds of help available locally or she may want something which is not available. In the latter case, make sure she is getting all she is entitled to before she arranges to pay for anything privately (see pp 46–47).

To get private help, she can advertise in a local newspaper or newsagent or a national magazine or newspaper such as *The Lady* or the *Daily Telegraph*. She should use a box number and take up references. Alternatively, she could use a private recruitment agency, which may charge a fee for finding someone. Local agencies are listed in the *Yellow Pages* under 'Employment Agencies and Consultants' or 'Nurses and Nursing'.

You might want to check that the organisation is a member of the United Kingdom Home Care Association (address on p 88).

FOR MORE INFORMATION

▶ Age Concern England Factsheet 6 *Finding help at home.*

▶ Carers National Association Information Sheet 24 *Getting alternative care at home.*

▶ **Counsel and Care** (address on p 81) has an automated information service which can provide names of nursing and employment agencies around the country.

▶ **The United Kingdom Home Care Association** (address on p 88) is an association of providers of care at home which can provide lists of member agencies.

Getting advice and support

Some of the main places you can turn to for advice and support are listed below. There is a longer list of useful organisations on pages 79–88.

Community Health Council (CHC) Information about local health services and advice if you want to make a complaint. Your local CHC will be listed in the local telephone directory, or contact the Association of Community Health Councils (address on p 80).

Citizens Advice Bureau (CAB) Information and advice on benefits, rights, housing, etc. Your local CAB will be listed in the phone book, or contact the National Association of Citizens Advice Bureaux (address on p 86).

Law centre Free legal advice. Ask at a CAB or contact the Law Centres Federation (address on p 85).

Community Relations Council (CRC) and **Council for Racial Equality (CRE)** Information and advice for black people and people from ethnic minorities. For the address of your local CRC or CRE contact the Commission for Racial Equality (address on p 81).

Carers' group or **self-help group** Information and help from other people in your situation – see page 50.

Age Concern See page 89 for more about Age Concern.

Carers National Association (address on p 81). Support, information and advice for all carers, plus many local groups.

▶ Carers National Association Information Sheet 21 *Coping with stress*.

▶ Carers National Association leaflet *End of your tether*.

▶ *Help at Hand* by Jane Brotchie, published by Bedford Square Press.

▶ *Taking a Break: A guide for people caring at home* by Maggie Jee, published by the King's Fund Centre, 126 Albert Street, London NW1 7NF. Tel: 071-267 6111.

▶ *Call for Care/Dekhbaal lai pukkar* by Yasmin Gunaratnam – information and advice for Asian carers of older people in English, Gujarati, Punjabi and Urdu. Available from the Health Education Authority, Hamilton House, Mabledon Place, London WC1H 9TX. Tel: 071-383 3833.

▶ *The Support You Need* – information and advice for Afro-Caribbean carers of older people. Available from the King's Fund Centre (address above).

CHECKLIST OF SUPPORT SERVICES AT HOME

Addresses and telephone numbers of organisations listed here can be found on pp 79–88.

Help with the daily routine	Whom to contact
Help with housework, shopping, cleaning	*Social services, voluntary organisation or private agency*
Help with getting up, getting washed and dressed, going to the toilet, eating, getting undressed, going to bed	*Social services or voluntary care attendant scheme (eg Crossroads) or private agency (contact United Kingdom Home Care Association)*
Help with incontinence or incontinence supplies (pads, pants, bedding)	*District nurse or continence adviser (ask the GP)*
Help with nursing, bathing, toileting, lifting	*District nurse (ask the GP) or private nursing agency*
Laundry service	*Social services (many local authorities no longer offer this service) or private laundry service (look in the* Yellow Pages*)*

Help with meals	Whom to contact
Meals on wheels	*Social services or voluntary organisation (eg Age Concern or WRVS – Women's Royal Voluntary Service)*
Luncheon club	*Social services, local community group, church or voluntary group*

Help with medical problems	Whom to contact
Advice about most general health problems	*Your relative's GP, who may refer her to someone else*
Nursing care at home, eg injections, changing dressings, etc	*District nurse (ask the GP) or private nursing agency*
Advice about lifting or turning someone heavy	*District nurse or physiotherapist (ask the GP)*
Advice on mobility and exercise	*Physiotherapist (ask the GP)*
Foot care, help with nail cutting	*NHS chiropodist (ask the GP or district nurse) or private chiropodist*

Help with aids, equipment and home adaptations	Whom to contact
Advice on equipment to help with everyday living, eg washing, cooking	*Occupational therapist (social services or hospital) or the Disabled Living Foundation*
Equipment for bedroom (rails, hoist, etc)	*District nurse or occupational therapist (social services)*
Mobility aids, eg wheelchair, walking sticks, walking frame	*GP, physiotherapist or hospital (ask the GP)*
Short-term hire of equipment	*British Red Cross, local Age Concern group, WRVS or other voluntary organisation, or private company – ask an occupational therapist or social worker or contact the Disabled Living Foundation*
Adaptations to make your home more suitable for someone with a disability	*Occupational therapist (social services), housing or environmental health department, or voluntary organisation (eg Care and Repair)*

Help with getting about	Whom to contact
Help with transport	*Dial-a-ride or other voluntary organisation, social services or private taxi*
Transport to and from voluntary luncheon club, day centre, etc	*Social services, community or voluntary group*
Transport to shops	*Community or voluntary group, Good Neighbour scheme (ask at social services). Some large supermarkets run a free bus service*
Advice about getting a specially adapted car	*MAVIS, Motability*
Orange parking badge	*Social services*
Disabled Person's Railcard	*Local railway station*

Social activities	Whom to contact
Day centre, luncheon club or social club	*Social services, voluntary organisation (eg local Age Concern or Alzheimer's Disease Society group) or community centre*
Holidays	*Social services or voluntary group (eg Carers National Association), Holiday Care Service*

A break for the carer (respite care)	Whom to contact
Someone to sit with your relative while you go out for a few hours	*Social services or voluntary organisation (eg Crossroads) or private agency (contact United Kingdom Home Care Association)*
Day care for your relative in a special day centre; may include lunch, social activities, use of bathing facilities, chiropody, hairdressing, etc	*Social services, hospital or voluntary organisation (eg Age Concern, Help the Aged or Alzheimer's Disease Society)*
Short-term care away from home, from a day to a fortnight. Could be in a hospital, hospice, residential or nursing home, or even another family	*GP, social services, hospital, residential or nursing home, Hospice Information Service, Holiday Care Service*

Help with aids and adaptations

Aids or adaptations might be needed to make your relative's home safer or easier to live in. If she is disabled, the local authority *must* provide disability aids and equipment, adaptations and a telephone if it is satisfied that she needs them (see pp 46–47).

Aids

Aids are gadgets and equipment that help people manage everyday tasks such as moving about, using the toilet, washing and bathing, dressing, cooking and eating. Examples are wheelchairs, commodes, special bath seats and taps, and two-handled mugs. Aids can improve the quality of life of people with a disability and allow them to remain as independent as possible. They can make the job of caring easier too.

If your relative has a physical disability or a mental disorder or illness, one of the hospital staff or someone from social services – usually an occupational therapist – should consider with her what aids might be helpful before she is discharged. There might be a home visit (see p 25). A physiotherapist may also advise on mobility aids. Essential equipment and aids can be arranged by the hospital staff or through the GP, district nurse or social services department. Equipment is usually provided free of charge or for a small fee.

Government guidelines on hospital discharge state that discharge procedures should ensure that '*any support, help, equipment required to enable the patient (and carer(s)) to cope at home is available by the time the patient leaves hospital*'. If essential equipment has not been provided, your relative can refuse to be discharged (see p 16).

If your relative needs an aid which isn't provided, she could borrow or hire it from a voluntary organisation such as the British Red Cross (address on p 80), or buy or hire it from a private company.

For further advice on aids, contact the Disabled Living Foundation or the Disabled Living Centres Council (addresses on p 83). They will be able to give you a list of disabled living centres, where you can go and look at what is available.

Telephone

If your relative doesn't have a telephone, she might be able to get help with the cost of having one installed from social services. The local authority must provide or assist in providing a telephone or any special equipment needed to use one to those who are regarded as disabled under the Chronically Sick and Disabled Person's Act. In practice, local authorities have very strict eligibility criteria and few people obtain this help (see pp 46–47). The Social Fund (see p 74) might also be able to help. British Telecom has a number of special services for older or disabled people. One of the organisations listed on pages 53–54 may be able to advise you.

Home alarm

You can get a home alarm connected to the telephone system. It is usually in the form of a pendant. You press a button and the call goes straight through to a control centre. This means that if someone falls or is suddenly unwell they can call for help without having to get to the telephone. A home alarm might be obtainable through social services or a charity such as Age Concern or Help the Aged (addresses on pp 89 and 84), or you can buy them privately.

FOR MORE INFORMATION

▶ Help the Aged Information Sheet 15 *Equipment for daily living.*

▶ Carers National Association Information Sheet 14 *Equipment to aid daily living.*

▶ Age Concern England Factsheet 28 *Help with telephones.*

▶ For more on BT services, dial 150 or obtain *The BT Guide for People who are Disabled or Elderly*, published by BT.

▶ **The Disabled Living Foundation** (address on p 83) produces a number of factsheets on aids and equipment.

Adaptations

Adaptations are changes to the home to make it easier or safer to live in. Some adaptations may be minor, such as a handrail next to the toilet. Others may be more substantial, such as installing a downstairs toilet.

Decisions about whether adaptations are needed should be made before your relative leaves hospital as part of the discharge planning process. Again, there might be a home visit.

NOTE The Government has said that *'any immediately necessary adaptations should have been made – or at least a firm timetable agreed – before a patient leaves hospital'*. Your relative should not be expected to return to her home if it is unsafe or impossible for her to live in it. The Local Government Ombudsman has upheld a complaint of maladministration by a local authority where aids were not available within three weeks of application (see pp 38–39 for more on how to complain). If essential adaptations such as widening doorways for a wheelchair can't be done in time, she can refuse to be discharged until the work has been done. See page 16 for more on this.

Some people can afford to pay for repairs and adaptations themselves. If your relative owns her own home, she may be able to borrow money against the value of the property. For more on this contact Age Concern England (address on p 89) or a home improvement agency such as Care and Repair (address on p 81).

Grants

If your relative lives in council housing, the housing department might make adaptations for her but there is often a long wait for this. Otherwise, it might help by giving her a grant for all or part of the work.

NOTE Grants are only available for work which has been approved by the local authority. If your relative starts the work before her application for a grant has been approved, she will be automatically disqualified from receiving a grant.

There are two types of local authority grant which it might be worth applying for: minor works grants and disabled facilities grants.

Minor works grants

These are for small repairs and alterations such as safety and security measures, putting in a downstairs toilet or loft insulation. Only owner occupiers and private tenants receiving Income Support, Council Tax Benefit (rate rebate in Northern Ireland), Housing Benefit, Family Credit or Disability Working Alliance can apply for them. The maximum grant in 1994–95 was £1,080. If the work costs more than that, you have to make up the difference yourself.

Minor works grants are **discretionary** – this means that the local authority can decide whether or not to award them. Unfortunately, in many areas local authorities do not have enough money to make discretionary grants, but it is always worth checking what's available locally.

Disabled facilities grants
These are for people with disabilities to help pay for adaptations such as changing the kitchen or making lighting and heating controls more accessible. Council tenants, private tenants, owner occupiers and landlords can apply for them. This kind of grant can be **mandatory** if an occupational therapist visits someone's home and decides that the work is essential – this means that the local authority has to give a grant if the person's income and savings are below a certain level. The size of grant will depend on income and savings.

For more information about these and other grants, contact the local authority housing department or a local authority housing advice centre.

Other sources of help with adaptations

▶ Social services might help pay for work not covered by grants to make the home safer, more comfortable and more convenient. If your relative is disabled, the local authority must help (see pp 46–47).

▶ It might be possible to get help from the Social Fund (see p 74).

▶ In some areas there are home improvement agencies which give advice to older home owners on adapting their homes. To find out whether there is one in your area, contact the local authority housing department or Care and Repair (address on p 81).

FOR MORE INFORMATION

▶ Age Concern England Factsheet 13 *Older home owners – Financial help with repairs.*

▶ Age Concern England Factsheet 33 *Feeling safer at home and outside.*

▶ Age Concern England Factsheet 12 *Raising income or capital from your home.*

▶ *An Owner's Guide: Your home in retirement*, published by ACE Books (details on p 92).

▶ *Using Your Home as Capital*, published by ACE Books (details on p 92).

4 On the day

For most people, the day they leave hospital is an important one. It is usually a sign that they are getting better and they may have been looking forward to going home for some time. But if it is not handled properly it can be a traumatic experience.

In this chapter, we take a step-by-step look at the arrangements that should be made for the day the person you are caring for leaves hospital and the kinds of things that can go wrong.

‘They hadn't asked him whether anyone would be there or whether he had a key. I think they must have thought I was telepathic.’

‘My uncle was in hospital for two weeks following a bad fall. He's 81 and lives on his own in an upstairs flat. When I visited him on the Thursday evening, he seemed fine and a nurse told me to telephone the ward on Friday at 2 o'clock to find out when he would be discharged. But at 11 o'clock on Friday I got a phone call at work to say that he was on his way back to his flat in an ambulance. I got a friend to drive over to where he lives in our lunch hour but by the time I got there the ambulance had been and gone because they couldn't get into the flat. I had his key so that I could get his flat ready for when he came home.

‘They hadn't asked him whether anyone would be there or whether he had a key. I think they must have thought I was telepathic and that I'd somehow know what was happening. Anyway, I rang the hospital and they said he was back on the ward but they would arrange another ambulance for him. They told me to wait at the flat. By the time he arrived it was about 4.30 in the afternoon and he was very distressed. I stayed with him over the weekend but by Sunday evening he was in such a bad way that I called his GP. He said he'd have to go back into hospital. Now he's back on the same ward in a very confused state.’

Notice of discharge

Some people are discharged from hospital with almost no notice. If they are keen to leave hospital they may not mind this, but your relative might need time not only to organise herself but also to adjust to the fact that she will be leaving the ward, where she may have made friends with staff and patients.

If you will be looking after your relative, you will also need time to get ready. You might have to organise a bedroom downstairs, arrange to have time off work, or sort out a rota of people to help you care for her.

Ideally, patients should be given at least 24 hours' notice before they are discharged. If you or your relative feels that you have not had enough time or that you are having to make important decisions in a hurry, talk to the ward sister (see p 20). If there is a genuinely urgent need for beds on the ward, your relative may be moved to another ward or even to another hospital, but she should not be discharged unprepared or unsupported. In its guidelines on hospital discharge, the Government has said that *'patients should not be discharged until the doctors concerned have agreed and management is satisfied that everything reasonably practicable has been done to organise the care the patient will need in the community'*.

Transport

Some people are able to organise their own transport home after a stay in hospital – on public transport or in a taxi. People on a low income may get help with paying for this.

But some people will find it difficult or impossible to arrange their own transport. If you or another friend or relative cannot provide transport for your relative, Government guidelines say that the ward sister and nursing team should arrange transport for her. This could be in an ambulance, taxi, hospital car or minibus. Or a volunteer from a hospital aftercare scheme (see p 51) might be able to drive her home.

If transport has been arranged for her, your relative should be told when she will be collected and kept informed of any delays. She should remain in the care of the nurses until the transport arrives, even if she no longer has a bed on the ward.

For frail or disabled patients who do not have anyone to travel with them, the ward sister and nursing team should arrange an escort for the journey. Volunteer escorts can sometimes be provided by hospital aftercare schemes, voluntary organisations and charities. If your relative is returning alone to an empty home, the escort should go inside with her to make sure she is all right.

Clothes, property and valuables

Your relative might need someone to bring her outdoor clothes into the hospital for her. If it is cold or she is very frail, she will also need blankets for the journey. A nurse should return property and valuables to her before she leaves.

Someone to be there

Some people are lucky and have friends and relatives to welcome them. But for someone who lives on her own, going home from hospital can be a lonely and frightening experience.

MAY 'The volunteer driver was very kind – he took my mother through to her back room, sat her down in a chair in front of the fire, made her a cup of tea and said cheerio. When she tried to get up her legs had stiffened up so much she couldn't move. She had to stay there all night – she couldn't even get to the bathroom or the phone. Luckily her neighbour called first thing to see how she was and she let herself in with the spare key.'

If you can't be there yourself, friends or relatives might stay for a few nights or neighbours may offer to call in during the first few days. In some areas hospital aftercare schemes have volunteers who can do this (see p 51), or your relative may belong to a local group or religious organisation which could help out.

Getting her home ready

If your relative lives alone, she may need some help in getting it ready before she leaves hospital, especially if she was admitted into hospital unexpectedly. Use the checklist below to make sure you have thought of everything.

CHECKLIST FOR GETTING HER HOME READY

▶ Are things generally in order: are there any dirty dishes to wash up? Does the house or flat need a dust or clean? Do the bins need emptying?

▶ Has she got her door key?

▶ Is the house warm?

▶ Has she got any cash? Has her pension been collected?

▶ Is there any food in the house? Someone might need to get milk and fresh food and prepare a simple meal for when she first gets home.

There might also be new hazards in the home to check. For example, if your relative is using a crutch or sticks, she will be more likely to slip on mats and rugs. You could fasten them with tape or remove them until she is no longer in danger of slipping. More substantial changes will take longer to organise (see pp 58–59).

NOTE Government guidelines on hospital discharge say that it is the responsibility of the ward sister and nursing team to ensure that *'for frail, disabled or elderly patients living alone arrangements have been made for their home to be heated and for food to be provided, where necessary, and that there is safe access to stairs and toilet and that it will be possible to gain entry'*.

Aids and equipment

The hospital should supply any essential equipment that your relative will need immediately such as:

▶ a wheelchair, walking sticks, crutches or zimmer frame;

▶ breathing equipment;

▶ a commode.

Training and/or fitting should be provided where necessary. Equipment supplied by the hospital should either be waiting for her when she gets home or should travel home with her. If she needs something that the hospital can't provide, it might be provided by the local authority or she might be able to borrow, hire or buy it (see p 57).

Notifying the GP

The hospital consultant should let your relative's GP know that she is coming out of hospital and inform her or him of any medical details or requirements. The Government recommends that written discharge summaries should be sent to GPs within 24 hours of discharge (by fax if necessary). Your relative may be given a 'discharge notification letter' for her GP, which will need to be delivered to the surgery. The GP may then arrange to visit her. If her health deteriorates or she is worried about anything, she can phone the surgery for further advice or you can do it for her.

NOTE If your relative is staying with you temporarily and hasn't registered with a GP in your area, you can telephone any local GP and ask them to visit if it is an emergency.

Medicines

The hospital should supply your relative with the medicines she needs until she sees her GP or goes back to the hospital. A nurse should explain to her:

▶ which medicines to take;

▶ when and how to take them;

▶ any side-effects to watch out for.

Government guidelines state that important points like this should be confirmed in writing (see p 30).

It's easy to make a mistake if you are taking several medicines. This can be dangerous as the amounts prescribed are carefully calculated and some drugs must not be taken with each other or must be taken at certain times of day. Some people find it helpful to keep a rough chart to make sure they don't forget to take a medicine or take one twice. The hospital might also be able to provide a 'dosette', a plastic dispenser for tablets with different compartments for each day.

If your relative has any questions about medicines, she can ring the hospital – she should have been given a 24-hour phone number before she was discharged – or she can ask her GP or a pharmacist.

Other instructions

Your relative should be informed of any symptoms to watch out for and where to get help if it is needed. She should also be given instructions if she needs to change dressings, administer eye drops or use an appliance such as a catheter. Or you or another carer could learn how to do this for her. She might have exercises to improve mobility or a special diet to follow. Again, Government guidelines state that important points should be confirmed in writing (see p 30).

Next appointment

If your relative needs any follow-up hospital treatment she should be given her next appointment in writing. If she is to attend a day clinic or day centre she should be told when she is to attend and how to get there.

If the day of discharge goes wrong

If you or your relative is not happy with the way the day she leaves hospital is handled, you can complain (see pp 36–39).

Discharge checklist

Government guidelines state that to ensure that all arrangements for discharge have been completed, *'responsibility for checking that the necessary action has been taken before a patient leaves the hospital should be given to one member of the staff caring for that patient. The member of staff should have a checklist of what should have been done.'*

This is an example of a checklist which nurses in one hospital use to make sure that everything has been taken care of on the day that patients leave the hospital.

DISCHARGE CHECKLIST

Name of patient:

Consultant:

Hospital number:

Unit:

Planned date of discharge:

Actual date of discharge:

		Date	Comments	Signed
Patient informed	**Yes/No**			
Relative/key carer informed	**Yes/No**			
GP informed	**Yes/No**			
Home visit	**NA/Yes/No**			

Transport home arranged	NA/Yes/No			
Outpatients appointment	NA/Yes/No			
Transport arranged	NA/Yes/No			
Medicines received	NA/Yes/No			
Self-administer/ person to administer	(specify)			
Dressings	NA/Yes/No			
Aids and adaptations ordered	NA/Yes/No			
District nurse requested	NA/Yes/No			
Health visitor requested	NA/Yes/No			
Social worker informed	NA/Yes/No			
Meals on wheels booked	NA/Yes/No			
Home help/home care booked	NA/Yes/No			
Day hospital/ rehabilitation unit	NA/Yes/No			
Packed meal	NA/Yes/No			
Clothes available	NA/Yes/No			
House key available	NA/Yes/No			
Pension book returned	NA/Yes/No			
Money/valuables returned	NA/Yes/No			

Specify other agencies to which the patient has been referred

Any other comments

Signature

FOR MORE INFORMATION

▶ Age Concern England Briefing Paper *Hospital discharge procedures*.

▶ Carers National Association Information Sheet 6 *Hospital discharge*.

▶ *Going Home from Hospital*, published by Home from Hospital (address on p 84 – send 75p with your order).

5 Managing money

Coming out of hospital can be an expensive time. Your relative might have to pay for extra things like special equipment or a special diet. You might have to give up work to care for her.

There are a number of different kinds of financial help for people who are being cared for and their carers. This chapter looks at the help that is available from the Government (State benefits) and local authorities. It also tells you how to take over your relative's financial affairs if she needs you to.

JEAN

6 Now I tell all my female friends to make sure they understand their financial arrangements in case anything like this happens to them. 9

'My husband had a stroke last year. There was no warning – one minute he was completely lucid and the next he couldn't speak or walk. Unfortunately, I had left it too late to talk to him about the money side of things. It had always been easier to let Norman get on with it. He was so good at that kind of thing. As long as we had enough money to pay for everything, I didn't really think about it.

'After his stroke it was a real nightmare trying to sort everything out. Norman had several pensions and investments but he obviously couldn't explain them to me and I couldn't make head or tail of all the paperwork. In the end, it was the health visitor who helped me make sense of it. She helped me claim Attendance Allowance for him and I get Invalid Care Allowance for looking after him.

'Fortunately, the house was in our joint names but I had to apply to the Court of Protection to be allowed to sell some of his shares.

'Now I tell all my female friends to make sure they understand their financial arrangements in case anything like this happens to them.'

Sources of financial help

State benefits

Claiming for benefits is not always straightforward, but you can get help and advice from:

▶ a Citizens Advice Bureau or another local advice centre;

▶ a hospital social worker or patient's welfare officer or someone from social services;

▶ a local welfare rights unit (see p 49) – they can do a benefits check to find out whether you are receiving all the benefits you are entitled to;

► the local Benefits Agency office (formerly the social security office – the Benefits Agency is responsible for paying State benefits).

The Benefits Agency publishes a range of leaflets which you can get from local offices, post offices and libraries. Some leaflets are available in languages other than English. It also has a freephone number (0800 666 555) which you can ring for advice and information. If your relative is housebound, someone from the local Benefits Agency office can visit her at home.

HINTS ON CLAIMING BENEFITS

► Let your relative's local Benefits Agency office know she is out of hospital.

► Ask whether she or you are entitled to any extra benefits.

► Claim as soon as possible – some benefits can't be backdated beyond the date of your claim.

► If you are in any doubt, claim anyway – you've nothing to lose.

► Get someone to help you claim or appeal if you are having difficulty – see list of organisations above.

Changes in benefits when your relative comes out of hospital

If your relative receives any State benefits, they may be affected if she is in hospital for more than a certain number of weeks. If she has been in and out of hospital, perhaps for respite care or chemotherapy, her separate stays in hospital may be added up and counted as one stay. So it is important to let the local Benefits Agency office know when she goes into hospital and when she comes out.

If you have been receiving a benefit for caring for your relative, your money may also be affected when she goes into hospital. If so, you will need to make sure that it is readjusted when she comes out.

FOR MORE INFORMATION

► DSS leaflet FB 2 *Which benefit?*

► DSS leaflet NI 9 *Going into hospital? What happens to your social security benefits or pension.*

► Age Concern England Factsheet 18 *A brief guide to money benefits.*

▶ *Your Rights*, published annually by ACE Books, a comprehensive guide to money benefits for older people (details on p 91).

Benefits for people who are ill or have a disability

Attendance Allowance

If your relative needs a lot of extra help when she comes out of hospital, she may be able to claim Attendance Allowance. This is for people who become disabled after the age of 65 or who become disabled at an earlier age but only make a claim after they reach 66. To qualify your relative must need help with personal care (such as washing, eating or using the toilet), supervision, or someone to watch over her. She should have needed this kind of help for at least six months – this can include the time she is in hospital.

Attendance Allowance is tax-free; it is normally paid regardless of income and savings and on top of any other benefits. There are two rates of payment:

▶ a lower rate for people who need help during either the day or the night;

▶ a higher rate for people who need help during both the day and the night.

Going into hospital

If your relative was already receiving Attendance Allowance when she went into hospital, it would have stopped after four weeks but should start again when she goes home, providing she still needs the same kind of care. Let the local Benefits Agency office know the dates she has been in hospital or write to the Attendance Allowance Unit, North Flyde Central Office, Norcross, Blackpool FY5 3TA.

Disability Living Allowance

Disability Living Allowance (DLA) has replaced Attendance Allowance for people who become disabled under the age of 65 and make a claim before their 66th birthday. There is a **care component**, paid at three different levels according to how much looking after people need, and a **mobility component**, paid at two different levels according to how much difficulty they have in getting about. To get DLA, your relative should have needed help for the past three months. DLA is tax-free and is paid regardless of income and savings and on top of any other benefits.

Other disability benefits

Other benefits which your relative might be able to claim include:

▶ Statutory Sick Pay

▶ Sickness Benefit and Invalidity Benefit (from April 1995 the Government intends to replace these with a new Incapacity Benefit)

▶ Severe Disablement Allowance

▶ Disability Working Allowance

▶ Industrial Injuries Disablement Benefit

▶ Pneumoconiosis, byssinosis and miscellaneous disease benefits

▶ Constant Attendance Allowance

FOR MORE INFORMATION

▶ DSS leaflet FB 28 *Sick or disabled?*

▶ DSS leaflet DS 702 *Attendance Allowance.*

▶ DSS leaflet DS 704 *Disability Living Allowance.*

▶ *Disability Rights Handbook*, published annually by the Disability Alliance (address on p 83).

▶ **The Benefits Enquiry Line** is a special Benefits Agency freephone (0800 882 200) for people with disabilities and their carers.

Benefits for carers

Invalid Care Allowance

Invalid Care Allowance (ICA) is a taxable benefit for people who can't work full-time because they are caring for someone for at least 35 hours a week. If your relative gets Attendance Allowance or the middle or top rate of the care component of Disability Living Allowance, you might be able to get ICA. You must be under 65 when you first claim.

You will not get ICA if you earn more than a certain amount after expenses (£50 a week in 1994–95). Expenses include the cost of paying for someone to care for your relative while you work.

ICA is counted as income if you are getting a means-tested benefit such as Income Support, Housing Benefit or Council Tax Benefit. It is not paid on top of most other benefits. But it might be worth claiming even if you do not actually receive it, as it entitles you to the **carer premium**, an extra amount paid to a carer who is getting Income Support, Housing Benefit or Council Tax Benefit, and **National Insurance credits** to protect your entitlement to a State Retirement Pension.

NOTE If you get ICA it might affect your relative's benefits. If you're not sure whether to claim, ask the local Citizens Advice Bureau to work out what is best for you both.

Home Responsibilities Protection

If you are of working age, you may be able to get Home Responsibilities Protection (HRP) to protect your entitlement to a State Retirement Pension. If you get Income Support because you are looking after your relative, you will automatically get HRP. Otherwise you will have to claim for it. You will need to be looking after your relative for at least 35 hours a week and she will need to get Attendance Allowance or the middle or top rate of the care component of Disability Living Allowance.

FOR MORE INFORMATION

▶ DSS leaflet FB 31 *Caring for someone?*

▶ Carers National Association Information Sheet 10 *Invalid Care Allowance (what it is, who can get it, how to claim it).*

Benefits for people with low incomes

If you or your relative has a low income and savings below a certain amount, you may be able to claim the following benefits:

Income Support Helps with basic living expenses by topping up people's weekly income to a level set by the Government. Pensioners and people who are sick or disabled get higher amounts and carers may get a **carer premium**.

The Social Fund Makes lump sum payments to help pay for things like extra bedding or a washing machine.

Housing Benefit and **Council Tax Benefit** Paid by the local authority to help with the costs of rent and Council Tax.

Help with NHS costs Your relative may be entitled to free prescriptions and help with certain NHS costs. Ask her GP, dentist or optician.

Going into hospital

If your relative is in hospital for more than six weeks, her Income Support will be reduced. Let the Benefits Agency office know that she is in hospital and when she comes out so that it can be readjusted.

If she gets Housing Benefit or Council Tax Benefit, these will be reassessed after six weeks and the amount she receives may be reduced. Again, let the council know that she is in hospital and when she comes out so that it can be readjusted. She can continue to receive benefit for up to 52 weeks providing she intends to return to her home and is not sub-letting it to anyone else. After 52 weeks she can no longer qualify.

If your relative is unsure about her position, get advice from one of the people listed on pages 70 and 71.

FOR MORE INFORMATION

▶ Age Concern England Factsheet 25 *Income Support and the Social Fund*.

▶ Age Concern England Factsheet 17 *Housing Benefit and Council Tax Benefit*.

▶ Department of Health leaflet AB 11 *Help with NHS costs*.

▶ DSS leaflet NI 9 *Going into hospital? What happens to your social security benefits or pension*.

State Retirement Pension

If your relative receives a State Retirement Pension, this will normally be reduced if she is in hospital for six weeks. Let the local Benefits Agency office know that she is in hospital and when she comes out so that her pension can be readjusted.

FOR MORE INFORMATION

▶ DSS leaflet NP 46 *A guide to retirement pensions*.

▶ Age Concern England Factsheet 20 *National Insurance contributions and qualifying for a pension*.

- *The Pensions Handbook*, published by ACE Books (details on p 92).
- For general advice on State Retirement Pensions, ring the Pensions Customer Service Line on 091-225 3439.

Help with your mortgage

If you or your relative finds your income is reduced as a result of her going into hospital, and you have difficulty keeping up your mortgage payments, you should tell the building society or lender as soon as possible. If you are worried about approaching the lender direct, get advice from a local Citizens Advice Bureau or housing advice centre. National Debtline (021-359 8501) can give you free and confidential advice.

If you receive Income Support, you may be able to get help with your mortgage.

FOR MORE INFORMATION
- *Assistance with mortgage repayments*, free booklet published by the Council of Mortgage Lenders, 3 Savile Row, London W1X 1AF. Tel: 071-437 0655.

Managing your relative's money

If your relative is unable to manage her own financial affairs when she comes out of hospital she may want you to manage them for her.

Collecting a pension or other benefits

If your relative collects her pension or other benefits from the post office, you or someone else can collect them for her by becoming her **agent**. To do this, she should write your name on the back of the payment order and sign it. If she wants someone to collect her money regularly, you can get an **agency card** from the local Benefits Agency office.

If your relative is not capable of understanding what she is doing, the Benefits Agency can appoint you to claim and collect pensions for her and spend the money on her behalf.

▶ DSS leaflet AP 1 *A helping hand: How you can help friends or relatives claim social security.*

Bank and building society accounts

If you need access to your relative's bank or building society account, perhaps to pay bills for her, either you could open a joint account or she can give you a **third party mandate** to operate her account. To do this she needs to write to the bank or building society giving you her authority. If she later becomes unable to understand what is going on, you should not continue to use the third party mandate.

Power of attorney

If your relative wants you to take over her affairs completely, for example in order to sell her house for her, she will need to give you a power of attorney giving you the legal right to act on her behalf. She can get a solicitor to draw one up for her or use a pre-printed form from a legal stationers.

Obviously, you and your relative will need to discuss a major step like this. If she is confused or forgetful, try to explain what you are suggesting and why. You might both want to get independent advice from a solicitor or a Citizens Advice Bureau before you go ahead.

An **ordinary power of attorney** becomes invalid if the person giving it becomes mentally incapable of understanding what she is doing. It is therefore a good idea for your relative to create an **enduring power of attorney**, which gives you the right to continue managing her affairs even if she becomes mentally incapable.

Martin 'My wife got Alzheimer's when she was 62. At the beginning she still had lucid periods and we were able to discuss the future together. We both agreed that taking out an enduring power of attorney was for the best.'

Court of Protection

If your relative is already mentally incapable of making the decision to give you power of attorney, you will have to apply to the Court of Protection (address on p 82) for permission to act on her behalf. The Court may then appoint you as a **receiver**.

If her affairs are straightforward and her income and savings small, it may make a **short procedure order** authorising her assets to be used in a certain way for her benefit.

In Northern Ireland, apply to the Office of Care and Protection (address on p 82). In Scotland, you have to go through a solicitor or accountant.

FOR MORE INFORMATION

▶ *Enduring Powers of Attorney*, available free from the Court of Protection. Send a large sae to the address on page 82.

▶ Age Concern England Factsheet 22 *Legal arrangements for managing financial affairs*. (If you live in Scotland, contact Age Concern Scotland for a copy of their factsheet – address on p 89.)

▶ *Managing Other People's Money*, published by ACE Books (details on p 91).

Useful addresses

Some of these organisations have regional offices which are not included for reasons of space. Contact the England head office of an organisation to find out if there are any regional offices.

Alzheimer Scotland –
Action on Dementia
Information and advice for people caring for someone with dementia in Scotland.

8 Hill Street
Edinburgh EH2 3JZ
Tel: 031-225 1453
Helpline:
031-220 6155 (24 hours)

Alzheimer's Disease Society
Supports families and carers, provides information about all forms of dementia and runs local groups.

Gordon House
10 Greencoat Place
London SW1P 1PH
Tel: 071-306 0606

Arthritis and Rheumatism Council
for Research
Information about arthritis and rheumatism.

PO Box 177
Chesterfield
Derbyshire S41 7TQ
Tel: 0246 558033

Arthritis Care
Advice and information about living with arthritis. Local branches in many areas for people with arthritis and their carers.

18 Stephenson Way
London NW1 2HD
Tel: 071-916 1500
(counselling
10 am–4 pm weekdays)
Helpline: 0800 289 170
(12–4 pm weekdays)

Association of Charity Officers
Advice on getting help
from charities.

c/o RICS
Benevolent Fund Ltd
1st Floor
Tavistock House North
Tavistock Square
London WC1H 9RJ
Tel: 071-383 5557

Association of Community
Health Councils
Information about your local
Community Health Council.

30 Drayton Park
London N5 1PB
Tel: 071-609 8405

BACUP (British Association of
Cancer United Patients)
Advice, information and counselling
for people with cancer and their carers.
Freephone helpline for people outside
London 0800 181 199.

3 Bath Place
Rivington Street
London EC2A 3JR
Tel: 071-696 9003

British Diabetic Association
Advice and information for people
with diabetes and their carers.

10 Queen Anne Street
London W1M 0BD
Tel: 071-323 1531

British Heart Foundation
Advice and information on all
aspects of heart disease.

14 Fitzhardinge Street
London W1H 4DH
Tel: 071-935 0185

British Red Cross
Various services provided by
volunteers including home nursing,
transport, holidays and equipment
loan. Local branches in many areas.

9 Grosvenor Crescent
London SW1X 7EJ
Tel: 071-235 5454

Cancer Relief Macmillan Fund
Specialist nursing for people with
cancer; financial grants;
short-stay homes.

Anchor House
15–19 Britten Street
London SW3 3TZ
Tel: 071-351 7811

CancerLink
Information and advice on all
aspects of cancer.

17 Britannia Street
London WC1X 9JN
Tel: 071-833 2451

Care and Repair Ltd
Specialist advice and practical help
on home repairs and improvements.

Castle House
Kirtley Drive
Nottingham NG7 1LD
Tel: 0602 799091

Carers National Association
Support, advice and information for
all carers. Information sheets and
other publications. A national network
of local carers' support groups.

20–25 Glasshouse Yard
London EC1A 4JS
Tel: 071-490 8818
CarersLine: 071-490 8898
(1–4 pm weekdays)

Charity Search
Free information about help
from charities.

25 Portview Road
Avonmouth
Bristol BS11 9LD
Tel: 0272 824060

Coloplast Advisory Service
Information and advice on
continence care, wound care and
stoma care. Factsheets and
publications.

Freepost
Peterborough
Business Park
Peterborough PE2 6BR
Continence care and
wound care
freephone: 0800 622 124
Stoma care
freephone: 0800 220 622

Commission for Racial Equality
Information about your local
Community Relations Council or
Council for Racial Equality.

Elliot House
10–12 Allington Street
London SW1E 5EH
Tel: 071-828 7022

Continence Foundation
Advice and information
on incontinence.

The Basement
2 Doughty Street
London WC1N 2PH
Tel: 071-404 6875

Counsel and Care
Advice and information for older
people and their carers, particularly
on residential and nursing home care.
Can sometimes give financial help to
older people who need care.

Twyman House
16 Bonny Street
London NW1 9PG
Tel: 071-485 1566

Court of Protection
*Information about power of attorney,
enduring power of attorney and
managing someone else's affairs
for them.*

Enquiries and
Acceptance Branch
Public Trust Office
Protection Division
Stewart House
24 Kingsway
London WC2B 6JX
Tel: 071-269 7034

Northern Ireland

Office of Care
and Protection
Royal Courts of Justice
Chichester Street
Belfast BT1 3JF
Tel: 0232 235111

Crossroads Care
*For a care attendant to look after your
relative and give you a break. The
service is free but not everyone
qualifies. Sometimes contracted by
social services to provide emergency
care.*

10 Regent Street
Rugby
Warwickshire CV21 2PN
Tel: 0788 573653

Department of Health
*For Department of Health
publications.*

Health Publications Unit
Heywood Stores
Manchester Road
Heywood
Lancashire OL10 2PZ

**DIAL UK (Disablement Information
and Advice Line)**
*Information and advice for people
with disabilities and their carers.
National network of local groups.*

Park Lodge
St Catherine's Hospital
Tickhill Road
Balby
Doncaster DN4 8QN
Tel: 0302 310123

**Dial-a-Ride and Taxicard Users'
Association (DART)**
*Information about local dial-a-ride
and taxicard schemes. Campaigns
for accessible public transport.*

St Margaret's
25 Leighton Road
London NW5 2QD
Tel: 071-482 2325

DIEL (Advisory Committee on Telecommunications for Disabled and Elderly People)
Advice and information on telephones for older people and people with disabilities and their carers.

Room 2/3
50 Ludgate Hill
London EC4M 7JJ
Tel: 071-634 8700

Disability Action
Information and advice for people with disabilities and their carers in Northern Ireland.

2 Annadale Avenue
Belfast BT7 3UR
Tel: 0232 491011

Disability Alliance Education and Research Association
Advice and information on welfare benefits (Mon 2–4 pm, Tues 2–4 pm, Thurs 10.30 am–12.30 pm).

Universal House
88–94 Wentworth Street
London E1 7SA
Tel: 071-247 8776
Welfare benefits enquiries:
071-247 8763

Disability Law Service
Free legal advice for people with disabilities and their carers.

16 Princeton Street
London WC1R 4BB
Tel: 071-831 8031

Disability Scotland
Information and advice for people with disabilities and their carers in Scotland.

Princes House
5 Shandwick Place
Edinburgh EH2 4RG
Tel: 031-229 8632

Disabled Living Centres Council
Information about local disabled living centres, where you can look at and try out aids and equipment.

286 Camden Road
London N7 0BJ
Tel: 071-700 1707

Disabled Living Foundation
Information and advice about aids and equipment.

380–384 Harrow Road
London W9 2HU
Tel: 071-289 6111

Health Service Ombudsman
For a booklet explaining the complaints procedure phone 071-276 2035.

Church House
Great Smith Street
London SW1P 3BW
Tel: 071-276 3000

Hearing Concern
Information and support for people
with hearing loss.

7–11 Armstrong Road
London W3 7JL
Tel: 081-743 1110

Help for Health Trust
Details of self-help groups and
publications about disabilities
and health problems.

Highcroft Cottage
Romsey Road
Winchester
Hampshire SO22 5DH
Admin: 0962 849100
Helpline: 0345 678679

Help the Aged
Information and advice for older
people and their carers. Information
sheets and other publications.
Home alarms and community
transport vehicles.

16–18 St James's Walk
London EC1R 0BE
Tel: 071-253 0253
SeniorLine: 0800 298 494
(10 am–4 pm weekdays)
Winter Warmth Line:
0800 838 587
(October–March)

Holiday Care Service
Information and advice on holidays
for older people and their carers.

2 Old Bank Chambers
Station Road
Horley
Surrey RH6 9HW
Tel: 0293 774535

Home from Hospital
Advice and information on
coming out of hospital.

20 Westfield Road
Edgbaston
Birmingham B15 3QG
Tel: 021-454 7894

Hospice Information Service
Information about local hospices
which care for people who are
terminally ill.

St Christopher's Hospice
51–59 Lawne Park Road
Sydenham
London SE26 6DZ
Tel: 081-778 9252

John Groom's Association
for the Disabled
Provides residential, respite and
holiday accommodation for people
with disabilities.

10 Gloucester Drive
Finsbury Park
London N4 2LP
Tel: 081-802 7272

Law Centres Federation
*Information about law centres
in your area.*

Duchess House
18–19 Warren Street
London W1P 5DB
Tel: 071-387 8570

Leonard Cheshire Foundation
*Residential homes, respite care and
home care services for older people
and people with disabilities.*

26–29 Maunsel Street
London SW1P 2QN
Tel: 071-828 1822

Local Government Ombudsman
*Looks into cases of maladministration
by local authorities that cause injuries.*

21 Queen Anne's Gate
London SW1H 9BU
Tel: 071-915 3210

Marie Curie Cancer Care
*Specialist nursing and nursing
homes for cancer patients.*

28 Belgrave Square
London SW1X 8QG
Tel: 071-235 3325

**MAVIS (Mobility Advice and
Vehicle Information Service)**
*Information on transport for people
with disabilities and advice on car
adaptations for passengers.*

Department of Transport
Transport Research
Laboratory
Old Wokingham Road
Crowthorne
Berkshire RG11 6AU
Tel: 0344 770456

**MENCAP (Royal Society for Mentally
Handicapped Children and Adults)**
*Information and support for carers of
people with learning disabilities.
Provides residential care, leisure
facilities, holidays and legal services.*

123 Golden Lane
London EC1Y 0RT
Tel: 071-454 0454

**MIND (National Association
for Mental Health)**
*Information and support for carers of
people with mental health problems.
Local associations provide counselling,
drop-in centres and other services.*

Granta House
15–19 Broadway
London E15 4BQ
Tel: 081-519 2122

Motability
Cars and wheelchairs for
people with disabilities.

2nd Floor
Gate House
Westgate
Harlow
Essex CM20 1HR
Tel: 0279 635666

National Association of Citizens
Advice Bureaux (NACAB)
Information about your local
Citizens Advice Bureau.

Myddleton House
115–123 Pentonville Road
London N1 9LZ
Tel: 071-833 2181

National Association of Councils for
Voluntary Service (NACVS)
Information about local Councils for
Voluntary Service, which can put
volunteers in touch with people
needing help.

3rd Floor
Arundel Court
177 Arundel Street
Sheffield S1 2NU
Tel: 0742 786636

National Council for Voluntary
Organisations (NCVO)
Information about voluntary
organisations.

Regents Wharf
8 All Saints Street
London N1 9RL
Tel: 071-713 6161

Northern Ireland Association
for Mental Health
Information about services for people
with mental health problems in
Northern Ireland.

80 University Street
Belfast BT7 1HE
Tel: 0232 328474

Parkinson's Disease Society
Information and advice for people
with Parkinson's disease and their
carers; local groups.

22 Upper Woburn Place
London WC1H 0RA
Tel: 071-383 3513

Partially Sighted Society
Information, advice and aids for
partially sighted people and their
carers. Runs the Low Vision Advice
Service on 071-372 1551
or 0392 210656.

Queens Road
Doncaster
South Yorkshire DN1 2NX
Tel: 0302 323132

Patients' Association
Information and advice on issues such as patients' rights, complaints procedures and self-help groups.

18 Victoria Park Square
London E2 9PF
Tel: 081-981 5676

RADAR (Royal Association for Disability and Rehabilitation)
Information and advice on aids and mobility, holidays, housing, sport and leisure for people with disabilities.

12 City Forum
250 City Road
London EC1V 8AF
Tel: 071-250 3222

Royal National Institute for the Blind (RNIB)
Information and advice for blind people and their carers.

224 Great Portland Street
London W1N 6AA
Tel: 071-388 1266

Royal National Institute for Deaf People (RNID)
Information and advice for people with hearing problems and their carers.

105 Gower Street
London WC1E 6AH
Tel: 071-387 8033

Scottish Association for Mental Health
Information about services for people with mental health problems in Scotland.

Atlantic House
38 Gardner's Crescent
Edinburgh EH3 8DQ
Tel: 031-229 9687

Scottish Council for Voluntary Organisations
Information about voluntary organisations in Scotland.

18–19 Claremont Crescent
Edinburgh EH7 4QD
Tel: 031-556 3882

Self-Help Centre
Information about local self-help groups and how to set one up.

Regents Wharf
8 All Saints Street
London N1 9RL
Tel: 071-713 6161

Standing Conference of Ethnic Minority Senior Citizens
Information, support and advice for older people from ethnic minorities and their carers.

5 Westminster Bridge Road
London SE1 7XW
Tel: 071-928 0095

Stroke Association
Information and advice for people who have had a stroke and their carers.

123–127 Whitecross Street
London EC1Y 8JJ
Tel: 071-490 7999

Tenovus
Emotional support and information on all aspects of cancer for patients and their families and friends; bilingual service for the people of Wales.

Cancer Information Centre
142 Whitchurch Road
Cardiff CF4 3NA
Tel: 0222 619846
Helpline: 0800 526 527

United Kingdom Home Care Association (UKHCA)
Information about private and voluntary agencies for home care in your area.

42 Banstead Road
Carshalton Beeches
Surrey SM5 3NW
Tel: 081-770 3658

Wales Council for the Blind
Information and support for blind people and their families in Wales.

Shand House
20 Newport Road
Cardiff CF2 1YB
Tel: 0222 473954

Wales Council for the Deaf
Information and support for deaf and hearing-impaired people and their families in Wales.

Maritime Offices
Woodland Terrace
Maesycoed
Pontypridd
Mid Glamorgan CF37 1DZ
Tel: 0443 485687

Wales Council for Voluntary Action
Information about local voluntary organisations in Wales.

Llys Ifor
Crescent Road
Caerphilly
Mid Glamorgan CF8 1XL
Tel: 0222 869224

Women's Royal Voluntary Service (WRVS)
Provides meals on wheels for older people in some areas.

234–244 Stockwell Road
London SW9 9SP
Tel: 071-416 0146

About Age Concern

Caring in a Crisis: Going home from hospital is one of a wide range of publications produced by Age Concern England, the National Council on Ageing. Age Concern England is actively engaged in training, information provision, fundraising and campaigning for retired people and those who work with them, and also in the provision of products and services such as insurance for older people.

A network of over 1,400 local Age Concern groups, with the support of around 250,000 volunteers, aim to improve the quality of life for older people and develop services appropriate to local needs and resources. These include advice and information, day care, visiting services, transport schemes, clubs, and specialist facilities for older people who are physically and mentally frail.

Age Concern England is a registered charity dependent on public support for the continuation and development of its work.

Age Concern England
1268 London Road
London SW16 4ER

Tel: 081-679 8000

Age Concern Cymru
4th Floor
1 Cathedral Road
Cardiff CF1 9SD
Tel: 0222 371566

Age Concern Scotland
54a Fountainbridge
Edinburgh EH3 9PT

Tel: 031-228 5656

Age Concern Northern Ireland
3 Lower Crescent
Belfast BT7 1NR
Tel: 0232 245729

Other books in this series

What to do and who to turn to
Marina Lewycka
At some point in their lives millions of people find themselves suddenly responsible for organising the care of an older person with a health crisis. All too often such carers have no idea what services are available or who can be approached for support. This book is designed to act as a first point of reference in just such an emergency, signposting readers on to many more detailed, local sources of advice.

£6.95   0–86242–136–5

Caring for someone who is dying
Penny Mares
Confronting the knowledge that a loved one is going to die soon is always a moment of crisis. And the pain of the news can be compounded by the need to take responsibility for the care and support given in the last months and weeks. This book attempts to help readers cope with their emotions and make all the necessary practical arrangements.

£6.95   0–86242–158–6

Finding and paying for residential and nursing home care
Marina Lewycka
Acknowledging that an older person needs to go into a care home often represents a major crisis for family and friends. This book provides a practical step-by-step guide to the decisions which have to be made and the help which is available.

£5.95   0–86242–157–8

Publications from ◆ⒶⒸⒺ◆ Books

A wide range of titles is published by Age Concern England under the ACE Books imprint.

Health and Care

The Community Care Handbook: The new system explained
Barbara Meredith

The delivery of care in the community has changed dramatically as a result of recent legislation, and continues to evolve. Written by one of the country's foremost experts, this book explains the background to the reforms, what they are, how they operate and who they affect.

£11.95   0–86242–121–7

Money Matters

Your Rights: A guide to money benefits for older people
Sally West

A highly acclaimed annual guide to the State benefits available to older people. Contains current information on Income Support, Housing Benefit, Council Tax Benefit and Retirement Pensions, among other sources of financial help, and includes advice on how to claim them.

For further information, please telephone 081-679 8000.

Managing Other People's Money
Penny Letts

The management of money and property is usually a personal and private matter. However, there may come a time when someone else has to take over on either a temporary or a permanent basis. This book looks at the circumstances in which such a need could arise and provides a step-by-step guide to the arrangements which have to be made.

£5.95   0–86242–090–3

The Pensions Handbook: A mid-career guide to improving retirement income

Jennie Hawthorne with Sue Ward

Many older people in their later working lives become concerned about the adequacy of their existing pension arrangements. This title addresses these worries and suggests strategies by which the value of a prospective pension can be enhanced. Advice is also provided on monitoring company pension schemes.

£5.95   0–86242–124–1

Using Your Home as Capital

Cecil Hinton

This best-selling book for home-owners, which is updated annually, gives a detailed explanation of how to capitalise on the value of your home and obtain regular additional income.

For further information, please telephone 081-679 8000.

General

Eating Well on a Budget

Sara Lewis

Completely revised, the new edition of this successful title offers sound advice on shopping and cooking cost-effectively and includes wholesome original recipes for four complete weekly menus.

£5.95   0–86242–120–9

Housing

An Owner's Guide: Your home in retirement

Co-published with the NHTPC

This definitive guide considers all aspects of home maintenance of concern to retired people and those preparing for retirement, providing advice on heating, insulation and adaptations.

£2.50   0–86242–095–4

To order books, send a cheque or money order made payable to Age Concern England to the address below. Postage and packing are free. Credit card orders may be made on 081-679 8000.

ACE Books, Age Concern England, PO Box 9, London SW16 4EX.

Information factsheets

Age Concern England produces over 30 factsheets on a variety of subjects.

To order factsheets

Single copies are available free on receipt of a 9″ × 6″ sae. If you require a selection of factsheets or multiple copies totalling more than five, charges will be given on request.

A complete set of factsheets is available in a ring binder at the current cost of £34, which includes the first year's subscription. The current cost for annual subscription for subsequent years is £15. There are different rates of subscription for people living abroad.

Factsheets are revised and updated throughout the year and membership of the subscription service will ensure that your information is always current.

For further information, or to order factsheets, write to:

Information and Policy Department
Age Concern England
1268 London Road
London SW16 4ER

Index

link workers *45*

local authorities *32 see* social services

luncheon clubs 55
    transport to 56

Macmillan and Marie Curie nurses *45*

meals: help with eating *54*
    provision of *46, 55*

medical care, help with *22, 25, 55, 66*

medicines, taking *66*

mobility aids *see* adaptations to homes;
aids and equipment

mortgage repayments, help with *76*

nurses: community psychiatric *44*
    district *21, 43*
    hospital *20, 21*
    Macmillan and Marie Curie *45*

nursing at home, help with *54, 55*

nursing homes *26, 28, 29, 32*

occupational therapists (OT) *21, 25, 49*

Ombudsman: Health Service *37*
    Local Government *38*

opticians *45*

Orange parking badges, obtaining *56*

OT *see* occupational therapists

parking badges, obtaining *56*

Patient's Charter 13

Pension, State Retirement: advice on *76*
    collecting for other people *76–77*
    reductions when in hospital *75*

physiotherapists *20, 22, 43–44*

powers of attorney *77*

private nursing agencies *52–53*

railcards, help with obtaining *56*

records, local authority *35*

recreational facilities, provision of *46*

Regional Health Authority (RHA) *42*

rehabilitation officers *21*

repairs, grant for *59–60*

residential homes *26, 28, 29, 32*

respite care *56*

RHA *see* Regional Health Authority

self-help groups *48, 50*

services *see* social services; support
services, home

Severe Disablement Allowance *73*

shopping: help with *25, 26, 54*
    and transport *56*

Sickness Benefit and Invalidity Benefit *73*

sign language, use of *22*

social activities, advice on *56*

Social Fund, the *60, 74*

social services *32, 46–47, 48–49*
    and care plans *21, 32–33, 47*
    complaining about *38–39*
    contacting *33–34* cost of *47–48*

social workers, hospital *21, 25, 48*

speech therapists *44*

Statutory Sick Pay *73*

stoma care advisers *44*

support services, home *54–56*

teeth, care of *45*

telephones, provision of *46, 58*

toileting, help with *25, 26, 54*

transport, help with *26, 56*
    from hospital *63*

United Kingdom Home Care Association *53*

voluntary organisations *48, 50*

walking frames, obtaining *55*

ward sisters *20*

washing, help with *25, 54*

welfare rights officers *49*

wheelchairs *26, 57*
    adapting houses for *12, 58*
    hiring *55*

Zimmers *see* walking frames